SIR WILLIAM DAWSON

Memoirs of the
AMERICAN PHILOSOPHICAL SOCIETY
Held at Philadelphia
For Promoting Useful Knowledge
Volume 84

# SIR WILLIAM DAWSON

## A LIFE IN SCIENCE AND RELIGION


CHARLES F. O'BRIEN

*Assistant Professor of History*

*Clarkson College of Technology*



AMERICAN PHILOSOPHICAL SOCIETY

Independence Square • Philadelphia

1971

12-6-95





Library of Congress Catalog
Card Number 71-153381

# *Acknowledgments*

I would like to express my deepest appreciation to Professors William G. McLoughlin and Léo Laporte of Brown University for the assistance I have received in working on this study.

The Staff of the Rare Book Room of the McLennan Library of McGill University was extremely helpful in facilitating my work on the Dawson papers. I am grateful to Clarkson College of Technology for funds to pursue my research.

I would also like to express my gratitude to Professor Lawrence Gelfand of the University of Iowa and Professor Edward J. Pfeifer of St. Michael's College for many years of advice, encouragement, and friendship.

CHARLES F. O'BRIEN

Potsdam, New York

# *Contents*

SIR WILLIAM DAWSON

# *Introduction*

A FEW DAYS after Sir William Dawson's death, on November 19, 1899, a memorial service was held in Montreal by some of his friends and admirers. The theme of the service was a text from Heb. XI, 4: "He being dead yet speaketh." The text was particularly appropriate, since Dawson's life and work had great meaning for these Montrealers. He had been for decades their most famous citizen, a pillar of the community and of the Bible they cited in his honor. He was their only scientist of international reputation. It was, then, understandable that his friends overestimated Dawson's posthumous appeal to those outside their community. Even in 1899, Dawson spoke to a rapidly diminishing audience and in the intervening years he spoke to almost no one.

Dawson did have something to say, however, although his significance was very different from that accorded by his Montreal admirers. Dawson still has something to say, but not as a scientific authority. His scientific work is completely outdated and, with rare exceptions, is of little interest to researchers today. Historians, who might have been expected to retain an interest in such figures, have been, for the most part, content to study the more notable scientists, especially those whose work has been vindicated by later research. Dawson certainly cannot be included in this category. Political and military history are often said to be written by the victors; much the same is true of the history of science. This emphasis is unfortunate and Dawson is one of a host of worthy scientists whose work deserves further study.

Dawson's career was a varied one and it is not only his scientific endeavors which merit study. His role in establishing a sound base for modern scientific research in Canada entitles him to more attention than he has received. His work in education, both as Commissioner of Education at a crucial period in Nova Scotian history and as the real founder of McGill University, deserves a separate study in itself. Both in Nova Scotia and at McGill, Dawson was a pioneer in emphasizing the sciences in undergraduate training. He impressed on McGill a tradition of scientific excellence which has continued to the present, for it is still the science faculties of this great university which are most renowned.

In this respect, Dawson was able to harmonize his own scientific pursuits with the larger needs of McGill. His emphasis on applied science had the very tangible effect of securing for McGill the benefactions of the Montreal business community. He was motivated, however, by much more than the canny instinct which often guides college administrators. The sources of this emphasis reveal the two sides of Dawson's life, the scientific and the religious. As an educator, Dawson was progressive, almost *avant garde,* in the introduction of a wide range of science courses to the McGill curriculum. At the same time, as an old-school Calvinist, he was motivated by perennial suspicion of the liberal arts. A dramatic example of this attitude was provided by Dawson's leadership of a secession from his Presbyterian Church when it introduced organ music into its services. For Dawson, man and his creations were corrupt. Since the liberal arts studied the work of fallen man, they were suspect. The sciences, for Dawson, escaped this taint because they studied the unsullied creation of God.

Dawson's career provides one more example of the impetus derived by science from the Calvinist outlook. He always saw the science curriculum at McGill and his own research as part of a religious quest. Exploring nature, for him, was much like reading the Bible; both were revelations of God's wondrous ways. Even when he was involved in seemingly unrelated controversies, such as the *Eozoön* and glacier questions, he remained alert for the religious implications of his work. Thus, *Eozoön* indicated the solicitude God showed His creatures. This much controverted fossil also provided, in Dawson's opinion, evidence of a gap in the paleontological record that was insurmountable for evolutionists. In a similar vein, he used the late Pleistocene shells of the St. Lawrence River valley to prove the statement of stability of species that he saw in the Bible's reproduction "after his kind."

Herein lies the most important reason for studying Dawson's work. His historical relevance in carrying on the search for a synthesis of the two theologies—natural and revealed—is much greater than his contributions to either education or natural science. Dawson's career shows the durability of the two theologies' tradition.

The view that God's will was revealed in nature as well as in Scripture has a very long heritage. However, this traditional attitude came into special prominence in the eighteenth century when Archdeacon William Paley succeeded in synthesizing Biblical Christianity, Newtonian science, and utilitarian philosophy. Paley's work, published between 1790 and 1802, was part of a reaction to the effective use by opponents of orthodoxy of the same philosophical and scientific points of view. The influence of Paley's synthesis was widespread and enduring. His books were commonly used as texts more than a generation after his death in 1805. The influence of his many followers continued even longer.

For example, what Paley did for Newtonian science, Hugh Miller and, to a lesser extent, Dawson himself did for uniformitarian geology. Their ingenuity was equal to the task of correlating the catastrophes and miracles of the

Bible with the uniformitarian doctrine of gradual change through existing, natural causes.

The synthesis of natural and revealed theology was considerably more difficult after Darwin. It was at this point that the two theologies' tradition broke down. Paley had convinced many that science, by showing the meticulous designs of the Creator, verified orthodox Christianity. After Darwin, when all arguments from design came under heavy fire, it became very difficult to secure even the most tenuous reconciliation of science and religion, let alone the details of Scripture. Perhaps despairing of again finding a synthesis of the Bible and science, religiously inclined scientists in the latter half of the nineteenth century tended, for the most part, to abandon the defense of the scientific accuracy of Scripture.

The two theologies' tradition insisted on incorporating scientific discovery and Revelation. In this sense the tradition of Paley differed sharply from both Fundamentalist theologians who shielded themselves and their theology from scientific discovery and from those scientists who completely ignored traditional theological formulations. The two theologies' tradition and Modernism occupied the middle ground between these two extremes.

Both the Modernists and the upholders of the two theologies' tradition attempted to harmonize science and religion. The Modernists adapted their theology to the new science. They emerged from the controversy over Darwinism with a theology which emphasized the principle of development in religious matters. For most of these evolutionary theists religious truth itself evolved; for some of them God Himself evolved. It has to be said that the latter day Paleyites, attacking the problem antithetically, failed in the end to accommodate the new science to the old theology.

His deep involvement in the two theologies' tradition led Dawson into controversy. The reassuring synthesis of science and religion that was so convincing in his youth seemed to be crumbling on all sides as he grew older. Attempting to reaffirm this synthesis, Dawson became one of the last great spokesmen for the two theologies' tradition. Dawson did not shrink from this rather lonely position, for he was preeminently a controversialist. His very life was woven out of controversy over what he regarded as the Word and the Work of God.

# I. A Life in Education and Science

WILLIAM DAWSON was descended from an old Scottish family, a family with a long heritage of Jacobite politics and Roman religion. Dawson tradition had it that, as a young boy, Dawson's grandfather had fought for the Pretender at Culloden. This fortunate forebear had escaped that bloody field and, afterwards, had married a Protestant wife and raised a family of Presbyterian children. In his later years, it was said, the former Jacobite was himself converted to Presbyterianism.[1]

The Dawsons were farmers and Banffshire was a hard place to farm, especially with most of the good land long since taken up. Consequently William's father, James Dawson, was apprenticed at a young age to a tradesman in nearby Huntly and, as soon as he was free of his apprenticeship, he emigrated to the virgin land of Nova Scotia. This was in 1811.

In a few short years James Dawson found the success that he was looking for in the New World. With proverbial Scottish acumen, he built a successful mercantile business based on the thriving Nova Scotia trade in lumber and fur. By 1818 he was even a shipowner. He married well and was a pillar of his community and church. When

[1] This chapter is based largely on Dawson's autobiography, *Fifty Years of Work in Canada* (London, 1901). I have also drawn on pieces of memorabilia in a scrapbook kept by Dawson and on two lengthy obituary articles by men who knew Dawson well. Frank Dawson Adams, author of the famous *The Birth and Development of the Geological Sciences,* was a student of Dawson and his successor as Logan Professor of Geology at McGill. Adams published an obituary in *Science,* N.S. 10 (December 22, 1899): pp. 905–910. Henry M. Ami, a member of the Geological Survey of Canada and another student of Dawson's, wrote a forty-eight-page biography and bibliography for *The American Geologist* 26 (July, 1900): pp. 1–48. I have also used personal interviews with Mrs. Lois Winslow-Spragge, a granddaughter of Dawson. Mrs. Winslow-Spragge had several vivid recollections of her grandfather and a veritable treasure trove of family lore.

his first son, John William, was born in 1820, James Dawson was a well-to-do man.

These good times did not last. James Dawson's fortune was lost in the wave of financial setbacks that swept over all of North America between 1819 and 1825. Young William Dawson, as he was to style himself in later life, grew up with no silver spoon in his mouth. His education was a very heavy burden for his parents to bear and was, in fact, interrupted so that Dawson could help with the family business. Dawson later recalled in his autobiography that a share of his first earnings went to remove the last of the debts his father had contracted some twenty years earlier.

Not long after the family's financial catastrophe, another more serious blow befell them. Dawson's younger brother, James, died of scarlet fever. Nearly seventy years later the pain of his brother's death was still fresh in Dawson's memory. He recalled, for instance, that he had refused some small assistance to James only a day before the latter's fatal illness struck. His brother's early death left Dawson an only child. This, combined with his father's financial misfortunes, resulted in a lonely and impoverished boyhood.

Despite these handicaps, Dawson received a good education. Presbyterians usually had a high regard for learning and took the lead in establishing educational institutions.[2] The Scotch Presbyterians of Nova Scotia were no exception. Despite the fact that the Pictou area was very recently settled, Pictou Academy was in full operation. The curriculum was based on that of similar Scottish institutions and was a rigorous one. Since Pictou Academy existed primarily to train the Presbyterian clergy of the area,

[2] Frederick Rudolph, *The American College and University* (New York, 1962), pp. 57–58. Rudolph notes, for example, that over twenty-five per cent of the colleges in the United States that survived into the twentieth century were of Presbyterian origin.

one of the rigorous courses was Hebrew. This early training in Hebrew stood Dawson in good stead when he began to apply his geological knowledge to Biblical exegesis.

Perhaps more important for Dawson's later career was his informal exploration of the geology of the Pictou region. He became involved in amateur geology at a very early age and explored the abundant coalfields, quarries, road-cuts, and coastal cliffs of the vicinity. Much of this early exploration was to remain useful throughout Dawson's life. The coalfields provided the fledging geologist with his first contact with the fossil plants that were later to occupy so much of his attention. One of the coastal cliffs that he explored was at South Joggins; these same cliffs provided the remains of *Dendrepeton,* discovered by Dawson and Lyell in 1852, the oldest reptile found in North America.

To this amateur background, Dawson was soon able to add more professional training. By 1840, the family fortunes had improved to the point that, with much sacrifice, it was possible to send young William to Scotland for further study. So, with an inquiring mind, an amateur's fervor and fortified by Lyell's *Elements* and *Principles,* De la Beche's *Manual,* and Phillips' *Elementary Geology,* Dawson sailed for Edinburgh in the fall of 1840.

Most of Dawson's work at Edinburgh was directly in geology. He studied chiefly under Robert Jameson. Jameson was an avid follower of Abraham Werner, the German mineralogist who believed that the earth had been precipitated from a great primeval ocean. It was Jameson who first translated Werner into English.

For an eager young man from the colonies the opportunity to study under a famous man such as Jameson was an exciting one. Edinburgh itself was a fascinating place for Dawson, who took full advantage of the extra-curricular offerings of the vicinity. He followed Scottish politics avidly and made a point of hearing the sermons of most of Scotland's famous preachers. In a less sober vein, he struck up an acquaintance with some distant relatives who lived in Edinburgh, the Mercer family. Dawson was especially taken by the youngest Mercer daughter, Maggy, whose name was to be successively dignified as "Dearest Margaret," Mrs. Dawson, and finally Lady Dawson.

The family financial difficulty again became acute in the spring of 1841 and Dawson's Edinburgh courtship of geology and Maggy came to an abrupt halt. He was not able to return until 1846. In the interim he worked with his father in the latter's bookstore and printing establishment and used his Edinburgh training in his spare time by making a geological survey of the coalfields of Nova Scotia. This five-year period was a most valuable one for Dawson. His survey of the coalfields gave him a great deal of practical experience and provided the basis for his important book, *Acadian Geology*. During this time he also made the acquaintance of the most famous geologist of the nineteenth century, Sir Charles Lyell.

Lyell came to North America in 1841 to see at first hand the geological wonders of the New World and, incidentally, to leave a very readable account of the conditions in the United States, *Travels in North America.* He went to Nova Scotia for the express purpose of comparing the coalfields of the colony with those of Scotland.[3]

It was a very pleasant surprise for Lyell to find a local authority on whom he could rely, whose training was respectable and whose enthusiasm was boundless. For Dawson, Lyell's trip provided an incomparable opportunity to study in the field with one of the world's greatest geologists. The interruption in his Edinburgh studies very quickly be-

[3] Charles Lyell, *Travels in North America* (New York, 1845) 2: pp. 149, 173–181.

came one of the most fortunate events in Dawson's life. Dawson and Lyell struck up an immediate friendship, a friendship that lasted until Lyell's death thirty-four years later. Lyell became Dawson's greatest benefactor, writing joint papers with him, proposing him for important positions, helping him to publish his research.

When Dawson was able to return to Edinburgh in 1846, it was as the protégé of a distinguished figure. It was five years since he had seen Maggy Mercer; they had corresponded but her letters had occasionally been very cool. Maggie's mother had not liked Dawson very well in 1841 and was hardly more fond of him as he became a really serious suitor. Maggy herself, despite the cool letters, soon fell in love with Dawson. When Dawson, his studies completed, returned to Nova Scotia in 1847, he did not go emptyhanded. Maggy's father, who did like Dawson, was loth to lose his daughter but is said to have declared that he "would rather Maggy in Nova Scotia with a full heart than in Edinburgh with a broken one." [4]

Though he came back to Pictou with more professional training as well as a young wife, geology was still a part-time occupation for Dawson. He spent the next three years in his father's book and printing business. Despite the fact that his attention was divided between business and geology, Dawson contributed a number of articles to major professional journals during this period—*The Quarterly Journal of the Geological Society of London, The American Journal of Science, The Annals and Magazine of Natural History,* to mention three. In 1849 he also delivered two series of lectures in natural history at Dalhousie College in Halifax.

[4] Family consensus has it that Margaret Mercer Dawson was but seventeen in 1847. Like many ladies before and since, she became increasingly vague on this point as she grew older. Mrs. Winslow-Spragge checked family memorabilia as closely as possible and arrived at 1830 as the probable date of Lady Dawson's birth.

This opportunity to lecture and make acquaintances in Halifax, the capital of the colony, was a turning point in Dawson's life. His lectures were very well received and in the audience were many of Nova Scotia's leading citizens. His temporary residence in Halifax brought him into contact with some of the figures in the colonial government. Joseph Howe, Provincial Secretary and, after Confederation, Prime Minister of the Province, took an interest in Dawson and offered him the position of Superintendent of Education for the colony. Dawson refused; Howe insisted; and Dawson finally accepted.[5]

Dawson's decision was probably the wisest he ever made. As superintendent he traveled continually throughout Nova Scotia. Travel was slow and laborious at best but, for Dawson, this slowness provided time for geological observation and enabled him to extend his study of the Pictou area —eventually beyond Nova Scotia itself to the entire Maritime area. The superintendency was also a chance for Dawson to establish a background in education. This he proceeded to do. In his active three years as superintendent he worked to introduce agricultural education in the colony and to establish a normal school for training teachers. When he left the post in 1853, he had the support of all Nova Scotia political parties. More important, he had left a permanent impression on Sir Edmund Head, then Lieutenant Governor of New Brunswick and soon to become Governor-in-Chief of Canada.

In the final year of Dawson's tenure as superintendent, Sir Charles Lyell visited Nova Scotia for the second time. This time his work with Dawson was truly memorable. Lyell and Dawson examined the famous erect fossil trees in the sea cliffs at Joggins. In the course of this work they discovered the remains of the oldest reptile recognized in

[5] Dawson, *Fifty Years,* p. 71.

North America. The fossil reptile turned out to be an entirely new genus—named *Dendrepeton* by the famous English paleontologist Richard Owen. *Dendrepeton* was soon the center of a small controversy; Dawson, Lyell, and Jeffries Wyman of Harvard held that it was a reptile, while the redoubtable Louis Agassiz insisted that it was a fish.[6] The discovery of *Dendrepeton,* the subsequent publication of descriptions and articles, the controversy (which was settled in favor of the reptiles) all served to give Dawson a modest but growing reputation.

In addition to this modest reputation Dawson had managed to obtain a very broad background. He had training and experience in both the practical and theoretical aspects of geology. He had an extensive apprenticeship in business affairs. To this he could now add three years of experience in educational administration. Equally important, Dawson had powerful friends in these same areas. He was a young man with a bright future.

This future arrived for Dawson in 1855. In that year he published his first book, and it was a major one. *Acadian Geology,* which went through four editions and numerous supplements, became a standard reference and remained one well into the twentieth century.[7] Almost simultaneously the chair of natural history at Edinburgh became vacant owing to the deaths in rapid succession of Robert Jameson and Edward Forbes. Lyell suggested that Dawson apply and offered his full support.[8]

Dawson faced formidable opposition for the Edinburgh post. At one time or another Hugh Miller, T. H. Huxley, and Louis Agassiz were in the field, to say nothing of a host of other applicants who were at least as well known

[6] Katherine Lyell (ed.), *Life, Letters and Journals of Sir Charles Lyell, Bart.* (London, 1881) **2**: pp. 183–186.

[7] J. William Dawson, *Acadian Geology* (Edinburgh, 1855).

[8] Lyell to Dawson, November 27, 1854, Dawson papers. Dawson scrapbook, p. 111.

as Dawson and who were able to press their cases personally. However, Dawson had Edinburgh connections of his own; his wife belonged to an old Edinburgh family; he had been a student there. Another factor in his favor was the recent publication of *Acadian Geology* which had been very well received. Most important of all, Sir Charles Lyell made the rounds of the scientific societies putting in good words on his behalf.

Dawson was one of the few who remained in the competition to the end. One of the most appealing aspects of Dawson to the curators of the University was his out and out Presbyterianism which contrasted sharply with the known agnosticism of Huxley. Agassiz, who was never seriously interested, was questioned for his polygenism; there were those who thought that Edinburgh should not hire a scientist who believed in more than one Adam and Eve! [9] Apparently there were also those who thought that the chair should not go to a young, untried colonial, for the curators chose George Allman, a man of established reputation who had been professor of botany at Dublin for ten years.

However, in 1855 Dawson had more than one opportunity for advancement and more than one patron. No less a personage than the Governor-in-Chief of Canada, Sir Edmund Head, took a hand to further his career. Without Dawson's knowledge, he suggested that the trustees of McGill University consider Dawson for the vacant principalship of that institution. For McGill the choice was a desperate one; it was either to find a good man or to give up the search entirely. As things turned out, the trustees chose very well indeed.

[9] Edward A. Lurie, *Louis Agassiz: A Life in Science* (Chicago, 1960), p. 192; Lyell to Dawson, July 20, 1855, Dawson papers. Lurie states that Agassiz was never interested in the Edinburgh job but kept open the possibility to increase his leverage at Harvard.

When the offer from McGill arrived in Pictou, Dawson was in Halifax preparing to sail to Edinburgh to press his candidature personally. He received the bad news from Scotland within a few hours of his scheduled departure. A few short hours after this disappointment, he received, totally unsolicited, an offer of the principalship of McGill from C. D. Day, president of the Board of Governors and a judge of the Supreme Court at Quebec. The post carried an annual salary of £500 plus a residence. For Dawson, the hand of Providence had written very clearly and he took the position, under the aegis of the most eminent man in Canada.

Dawson soon found that he needed all of the support that Sir Edmund Head could give him, for McGill was in a deplorable state. The initial bequest that provided money for McGill was made by James McGill, a wealthy fur trader, in 1813. McGill's bequest was contested by his heirs and the ensuing litigation stalled further efforts at establishing a university for eight years. Finally, in 1821, a charter was secured. Despite the charter and the end of litigation, McGill was not open for classes until 1828.[10] These fits and starts were but a sample of the difficulties McGill endured in its early years; by the time Dawson arrived in 1855 it had almost closed its doors several times.

If the academic outlook was gloomy, the other aspects of living in Montreal were not much better. The "residence" mentioned by Judge Day in his original offer to Dawson turned out to be in use as a chemistry laboratory. It took young Mrs. Dawson almost a year to remove the last vestiges of unsuccessful experiments. Montreal, a very provincial and isolated city in 1855, was scarcely more habitable. It had not yet become a major port and had no rail connections with the outside world. For several years

[10] Cyrus Macmillan, *McGill and Its Story 1821–1921* (London, 1921), pp. 98–154.

after Dawson's arrival there was not even a bridge over the St. Lawrence River. During the Christmas vacation in 1855 Dawson went to Toronto, then the seat of the Canadian government, to seek assistance for McGill. The 370-mile trip took five days—across the St. Lawrence by canoe, by train to St. John's, Quebec, and, variously, by train and sleigh to Albany, Niagara, Hamilton, and Toronto.[11]

The trip to Toronto was not successful; Dawson returned with empty pockets. Undaunted, he began to search out local benefactors and before long had secured considerable financial backing from the Molson family, owners of a prosperous brewery. Molson Hall was the appropriate name given the result of this benefaction, the first of many that this distinguished family was to make to McGill.

Fund raising was another activity to add to Dawson's growing list. Although he had not bargained for such duty, it was a function at which he became very adept. Family raising was a career Dawson had bargained for and this now became a much more formidable task. The Dawsons had five children between 1849 and 1858: George, William, Rankine, Anna, and Eva. They were, by all accounts, a very lively group and Dawson gave unstintingly of his time in family outings and educational field trips. With his eldest son, George, his educational attention involved much more than field trips. George was stricken with a "chill" (almost certainly poliomyelitis) which left him stunted in growth from early boyhood and made it impossible for him to attend regular school. He was educated almost entirely at home, by Dawson himself.[12]

[11] Stephen Leacock, *Montreal: Seaport and City* (Garden City, N. Y., 1942), p. 171.

[12] George was eventually able to go to the London School of Mines where he worked under T. H. Huxley and took top honors, and incidentally became a life-long friend of Huxley's son, Leonard. George was a remarkable man; despite his handicaps, he made many of the original geological surveys of western Canada and later became director of the Geological Survey of Canada. He was in many respects a superior geologist to his father.

Despite these distractions, Dawson produced an immense amount of original research in the years after 1855. In 1857 he published *Archaia,* an ambitious attempt to reconcile geology and Genesis. In 1859 he published a lengthy article "On the Fossil Plants from the Devonian Rocks of Canada" in the *Quarterly Journal of the Geological Society of London*—an article referred to by a well-known paleontologist, William C. Darrah, as late as 1960, in the following terms:

> Every student of paleobotany should examine this famous paper. . . . Despite the fragmentary nature of the specimens, Dawson's shrewd and critical judgment made possible a correct interpretation.[13]

In the next few years Dawson wrote several important articles on the materials he and Lyell had worked over at Joggins. By 1865 he was engaged in extensive research on the *Eozoön* question. A second edition of *Acadian Geology* was issued in 1868; the modest 388-page first edition grew to 694 pages when material from Dawson's interim research was included.

Nearly all of his work was carried on during vacations, for when McGill was in session Dawson had his hands full. In these early years he delivered about twenty lectures weekly and conducted courses in chemistry, botany, zoology, and geology. On his day of rest he taught Sunday School in the nearby Presbyterian Church. In addition, he executed his administrative duties in the grand manner. It was Dawson's custom to invite students with letters of introduction to private dinner at his residence. All McGill students came in small groups to "evenings" at Dawson's home. These affairs, involving light refreshment and informal discussions of science and Scripture, were dubbed by the undergraduates, "Tea and Fossils."

[13] William C. Darrah, *Paleobotany* (2nd ed., New York, 1960), p. 55.

These evenings of science and Scripture provide an indication of the direction in which Dawson's work was turning. He was throughout his life a devout Christian. His special concern was to show the majesty of God and His work in nature. His second book, *Archaia,* was an ambitious attempt to bridge the apparent gap between geology and Genesis. Dawson's work was in the great tradition of natural theology; he very painstakingly followed each word of the first chapter of Genesis and tried to find correlations with scientific knowledge. His views were based largely on those of the Scottish exegete, Hugh Miller. Dawson opposed the widely read theories of Edward Hitchcock, whose *The Religion of Geology* had been published in 1851. Hitchcock believed that the "days" of Genesis were only twenty-four hours long and that they did not refer to the original creation of the world but, rather, to the final arrangements. Dawson apparently never read a second popular American synthesis of geology and Genesis, Benjamin Silliman's *Consistency . . . of Geology with the Sacred History of the Creation and the Deluge* (1837).

After *Archaia* he turned his attention to the more pressing question of the evolution of species and the impact of Darwinism on Christianity. Dawson reviewed *The Origin of Species* when it was first published.[14] He also wrote critiques of the works of Gray, Hooker, Wallace, Huxley, and Haeckel as they were issued. Dawson's reaction to these works was, of course, negative. He saw the latest interest in evolution as no different from that of a generation earlier, the generation of Geoffroy St. Hilaire and of Robert Chambers' *Vestiges of the Natural History of Creation.* This earlier evolutionism had contained a large parcel of quackery and pseudo-mystical *Naturphilosophie.* For

[14] Dawson's review appeared in *The Canadian Naturalist and Geologist* 5 (February, 1860): pp. 100–102.

Dawson, Darwin and his adherents were tarred with the same brush.

Not content with reviewing evolutionist work negatively, Dawson began to search out anti-evolutionary applications of his own work. This search began in the mid-1860's and preoccupied him after 1870 as he became more and more a popular spokesman for the opponents of evolution. Dawson's work on Devonian plants had begun with a narrow focus; after *The Origin of Species* was published, this work was used as evidence of the early and abrupt introduction of highly advanced forms. *Eozoön canadense* first attracted Dawson because of the exciting prospect of finding life far down in rocks hitherto described by the discouraging term Azoic (lifeless). However, he soon became equally interested in the use of *Eozoön* as part of his refutation of Darwinism. In 1877, Dawson published a revised edition of *Archaia* under the title *The Origin of the World According to Revelation and Science.* The specific purpose of the new edition was to incorporate a lengthy attack on evolution in general and Darwinism in particular.

The anti-Darwinian cause also provided Dawson with his strongest temptation to leave McGill. Despite many setbacks, Dawson had been very happy at the university. In 1868 he had made a half-hearted attempt to obtain the principalship of Edinburgh but he showed none of the enthusiasm that characterized his earlier application there. Now, ten years later, the job was seeking the man. The specific appeal of Dawson was his opposition to Darwinism; the job was at Princeton.

Princeton was at this time a bastion of Old School Calvinism. Darwinism was anathema to Charles Hodge, for years the most influential professor at the theological seminary affiliated with Princeton. In 1874 Hodge had published a book with the enquiring title *What Is Darwinism?* and had answered his own question very bluntly: Darwinism was atheism. By 1878 Hodge had retired and was serving as chairman of the Board of Trustees. The position of the college's president, James McCosh, was discreetly equivocal. McCosh publicly maintained that evolution by means of natural selection was readily reconcilable with Biblical Christianity; privately, he seemed to have had some doubts.[15] The leading scientist at Princeton was Arnold Guyot, an associate of Louis Agassiz and, like him, a firm opponent of Darwinism.

Guyot was in ill health and was preparing to retire in 1878. He wished to have his responsibilities curtailed. Since Guyot held two chairs, physical geography and geology, the Board of Trustees, apparently at Hodge's urging, proposed that Guyot be relieved of his geological duties and that Dawson be offered that chair.[16]

The offer to Dawson was an attractive one: a salary of $3,000 per annum for College duties, a residence, and $1,000 for an annual series of lectures on the relations of science and religion at the theological seminary. McCosh wrote that the total salary of $4,000 was equal to his own and that the trustees were willing to pay more but were afraid of antagonizing others; "they have their hearts set on you."[17]

In addition to these inducements, wrote McCosh, a New York merchant who wished to remain anonymous was

[15] McCosh wrote a number of articles warning against a hasty rejection of evolution on religious grounds; he addressed Princeton undergraduates to this effect (Thomas J. Wertenbaker, *Princeton: 1746–1896* [Princeton, 1946], pp. 309–312). On the other hand, McCosh had an opportunity to hire Edward Drinker Cope and, according to Cope, refused because Cope was an evolutionist (Henry Fairfield Osborn, *Cope: Master Naturalist* [Princeton, 1931], p. 172). Most interesting of all in this regard is McCosh's anonymous publication of an anti-Darwinian article in the *North American Review.* The article, "An Advertisement for a New Religion," appeared in July of 1878, the very month in which Dawson refused Princeton's offer. Although signed "An Evolutionist," it is very critical of the irreligious tendencies of Darwinism. The article is attributed to McCosh in a bibliography of his writings contained in: William Milligan Sloane, *The Life of James McCosh* (New York, 1896), p. 276.

[16] McCosh to Dawson, March 23, 1878, Dawson papers.

[17] *Ibid.*

willing to provide funds for summer excursions to Wyoming and Colorado. This suggestion seemed to be directed at interesting Dawson in some of the professional acclaim this work promised. Edward Drinker Cope and Othniel Marsh had received much acclaim in a few summers spent antagonizing each other and uncovering evidence in support of evolution. More important, Princeton and its unnamed benefactor seemed interested in getting a qualified opponent of evolution into the great fossil beds of the West.

Dawson was interested and his interest must have quickened when, a few weeks after the original offer, McCosh indicated that Dawson could expect to have a hand in administering the new School of Science.[18] "I would expect you to largely form it," wrote McCosh.[19]

> The fact is that if you decline, which I hope you may not, we do not know where to look for a geologist of repute who is not a Darwinian. We feel it to be of vast moment not only for ourselves but for the country to have you in the United States to guide opinion at this critical time.[20]

McCosh seemed to think that Darwinians were all right as long as he did not have to hire them. He closed his appeal to Dawson by arguing that the offer was a "call" in the classic theological sense.

Two days later Charles Hodge wrote to Dawson and continued the theme of a "call." Hodge listed four reasons for Dawson's accepting the Princeton offer. With somewhat confused geography, he pointed out that the United States was larger than Canada and, hence, would provide a grander arena for Dawson's talents. Princeton, said Hodge, was a thoroughly Presbyterian institution:

[18] The background of Princeton's aborted School of Science is given in Wertenbaker, *Princeton*, pp. 307–309.

[19] McCosh to Dawson, April 4, 1878, Dawson papers.

[20] *Ibid.*

"All its Trustees are Presbyterians. All its Presidents have been Presbyterians." Dawson could, for the first time in his life, directly combine his secular activities with his professed faith. The warmer climate of Princeton would be healthier for Dawson's family. Most important in Hodge's view was the fact that "we are sadly in want, in this country, of scientific men who are firm believers in the Bible." "You cannot be more needed in Montreal than you are here . . . *damit ist viel gesagt.*" [21]

Dawson wrote later that these "inducements were strong, both in my own interests and in those of my family, but I disliked the idea of leaving my own country and allegiance and of abandoning a work which seemed so necessary." [22] The work which seemed so necessary to Dawson was the support of a "handful of Protestant people who are holding an advanced post in the midst of ultramontanism." This remnant was, in Dawson's opinion, threatened on the one hand by Romanism and on the other by the same spirit of materialism that so concerned Hodge. Dawson could not bring himself to "desert the friends who have fought . . . in this double-handed fight." [23]

There are several interesting aspects to the Princeton offer. It was a sign of Dawson's emergence as one of the last geologists of deserved reputation to oppose evolution uncompromisingly. His own position in geology was strikingly similar to that of the embattled remnant of Protestants in Quebec. The offer was also evidence of a conscious attempt on the part of the Princeton trustees, with the active connivance of McCosh, to erect an anti-Darwinian citadel at the college. Citadel is an especially apt word,

[21] Charles Hodge to Dawson, April 6, 1878, Dawson papers.

[22] Dawson, *Fifty Years*, p. 173.

[23] Dawson to Charles Hodge, July 15, 1878, Dawson papers. Hodge never received Dawson's last letter; he died on June 19. Dawson was at his summer camp at Little Métis near the Gulf of St. Lawrence and, consequently, did not hear of Hodge's death for some time.

for the rhetoric throughout the exchange of letters was military. Hodge and McCosh were calling Dawson into the fort. When he refused, it was because he insisted on remaining at the front. The refusal itself is intriguing, as well. Dawson wrote to Hodge, not to McCosh from whom the offer actually came.[24]

Defense of the saving remnant surely weighed heavily in Dawson's mind when he turned down Princeton; however, he had more tangible reasons for refusing. He seems to have used the offer to gain greater leverage at McGill. He seized the opportunity to demand that he be relieved of his teaching duties and that he no longer be responsible for the onerous task of supervising a normal school connected with the university. Dawson was also promised "new and larger benefactions." [25] The author of this promise was Peter Redpath, a wealthy Montreal sugar merchant who was already a generous donor. Redpath promised to provide funds for a museum and, possibly, a library.[26] He was as good as his word; both were built before Dawson's retirement.

Having committed himself to McGill for the remainder of his career, Dawson turned his attention to a wider scope of professional activity and continued his prodigious rate of publication. Princeton may have failed to obtain Dawson's teaching services; however, *The Princeton Review* received the services of his pen. He published six articles in the *Review* between 1878 and 1881; all but one were concerned with either evolution or the relation of science and religion. Dawson also continued to produce more narrowly scientific articles in the areas of his deepest interest—*Eozoön canadense,* glaciology, and Devonian flora. In these years of intense activity Dawson added three books

[24] *Ibid.*

[25] Peter Redpath to Dawson, April 5, 1878, Dawson papers.

[26] Dawson, *Fifty Years,* pp. 173–174.

to his growing bibliography: *Fossil Men and Their Modern Representatives* (1880), *The Chain of Life in Geological Time* (1880), and *Facts and Fancies in Modern Science* (1882).

Dawson was sixty-two years old when *Facts and Fancies in Modern Science* was published. His had been a well-known name in geology for more than twenty-five years. Popular books such as *The Origin of the World According to Revelation and Science* (1877), *The Story of the Earth and Man* (1874), and more recently, *The Chain of Life in Geological Time* (1880), had extended his reputation to a much wider audience. *The Chain of Life in Geological Time,* for example, went through nine editions and was popular enough to be pirated twice.

Dawson now began to receive public recognition for this work. He was awarded the Lyell Medal of the Geological Society of London in 1881. In the following year Queen Victoria, with particular appropriateness, made him a member of the Order of St. Michael and St. George. Dawson was the moving spirit behind the establishment of the Royal Society of Canada and, in 1882, he became the first president of the society. In that year also Dawson was elected president of the American Association for the Advancement of Science. The meeting of the association at which Dawson was elected president was held at Montreal and the leading social event was the dedication of the Redpath Museum. This was truly a year of remarkable achievements for Dawson. It was also an exhausting year. Dawson entertained extensively in his own home when the A.A.A.S. met in Montreal. Asa Gray and James Hall, among others, stayed with the Dawsons. An indication that Dawson's role as host involved extraordinary service was contained in a post-convention letter from Hall apologizing for breaking one of the Dawsons' lamps.

After many years of difficult work at an outpost of the intellectual world, the honors that fell to Dawson after 1880 must have been very gratifying. He was knighted in 1884. In the same year he served as host for the British Association meeting in Montreal. In 1885 he was elected president of the British Association and thus became the only man to serve as president of both the American and British associations.

Dawson continued to be active in the political side of science, to execute his duties at McGill and to pursue his research with undiminished vigor until 1892. In that year he suffered a severe attack of pneumonia and was forced to take a leave of absence from McGill in order to recuperate in Florida. He returned to McGill in the spring of 1893 and very shortly afterward suffered a stroke which left him partially paralyzed and made it impossible to carry out his responsibilities as principal. He therefore announced his resignation at the commencement exercises in May of 1893.

Dawson could look back on a record of tremendous accomplishment. When he arrived at McGill the University's very survival was in doubt; when he retired its place as one of the important universities in the world was secure. In addition to his own work, there was that of Sir William Osler who began his career at McGill. There would soon be the research of Ernest Rutherford and many other distinguished scientists and scholars, including two students of Dawson who themselves became eminent geologists, Frank Dawson Adams and Henry Ami. In 1855 McGill had sixteen faculty members, most of them part-time; thirty-eight years later this faculty numbered more than one hundred. During this period a dozen or more buildings were erected, among them a new library and the Redpath Museum. It is not without reason that the historian of McGill called Dawson the "greatest among the makers of McGill," [27] or that Stephen Leacock, who joined the McGill faculty only four years after Dawson's death, should have said of Dawson and his work at McGill: "Dawson was a great man, one of the great men of the nineteenth century. More than that of any one man or group of men McGill is his work." [28]

Following his initial stroke, Dawson's strength again returned. He was able to publish more than twenty articles after his retirement and continued to campaign on behalf of the organic origin of *Eozoön canadense.* He lectured at the Lowell Institute in Boston and published two books: *Some Salient Points in the Science of the Earth* (1894) and *Relics of Primeval Life* (1897). It should be noted, however, that both of these books consist largely of earlier work. In 1895 Dawson was elected to his last major office as president of the Geological Society of America.

After his retirement, he found time for more leisure at his home at Métis. His granddaughter, Mrs. Lois Winslow-Spragge, remembered him as spending hours walking up and down country roads, dressed rather formally. Her most vivid recollections of her grandfather were his brilliant blue eyes and the black Panama hat he always wore. In these years Dawson's favorite relaxation was to gather with his family around a bonfire in the evening at Métis. Another diversion enjoyed by Dawson was quizzing his grandchildren on the Psalms. Those who could recite them properly were rewarded with shiny new dimes. He scorned anything more frivolous. In fact, when a friendly clergyman suggested that Sir William take up golf in his retirement, Lady Dawson replied as tactfully as possible that she did not dare pass the suggestion on.

In 1896, although his health was again deteriorating, Dawson was well enough to attend the London wedding of

[27] Macmillan, *McGill,* p. 211.
[28] Leacock, *Montreal,* p. 298.

his youngest son, Rankine. During this last journey to England, Dawson found time to make a visit to a young paleobotanist named Robert Kidston who, along with W. H. Lang twenty-four years later, was to resurrect and validate Dawson's work on Devonian flora in a monograph described as "probably the greatest classic in paleobotany." [29]

After his return to Canada, Dawson suffered a series of strokes that severely curtailed his activities. He had to be carried from his home to the office he retained in the Redpath Museum. However, he occupied his time now not with museum research but with the Bible, awaiting the day and the hour. He died peacefully in his sleep in the early morning hours of November 19, 1899.

[29] Darrah, *Paleobotany,* p. 55.

# *II. Dawson and His Controversies*

The development of science in the nineteenth century far outstripped that of any previous period. The foundations of almost every branch of study were shaken by this spectacular advance. When the century opened, scientists were seriously discussing the proposition that the world had begun on October 23, 4004 B.C.; one hundred years later Rutherford and Boltwood produced convincing evidence that the world was at least two billion years old. The discrepancy between these two periods of time was just one indication of the radical changes in scientific outlook that took place in this turbulent century.

In 1800 biologists were largely ignorant of the nature of cells; the germ theory of disease was unknown. The research of Pasteur and Lister, work that is today common knowledge to elementary school students, remained to be done. In chemistry, the discovery of atomic weights and x-rays did not occur until the nineteenth century. More important, organic chemistry, with all that it has done to change our lives, hardly existed before 1800. In mathematics, much the same was true of non-Euclidean geometry. Physicists were unaware of the electromagnetic induction of voltage until Faraday's experiments in the 1830's. To appreciate the significance of these discoveries and the changes wrought in this century, one has only to think how much further this list could be extended and to consider the degree to which subsequent applied science has depended on such developments.

Advances in scientific knowledge on this scale were inevitably accompanied by much controversy. This was particularly true with the major developments in geology in the first half of the century. At this time geology was subjected to sustained and bitter controversies. In like manner the latter half of the century was dominated by the great dispute over evolution, probably the most fiercely contested of all scientific controversies.

In 1800 geologists were vigorously discussing the neptunist and vulcanist theories of the formation of the earth. The neptunists, led by Abraham Werner of Freiburg, argued that the earth had originally been covered by a great primeval ocean and that the rocks which formed the earth's surface had been precipitated from this ocean. The neptunists were still trying to explain what happened to all of the excess water when the vulcanists, led by James Hutton, asserted at the end of the eighteenth century that volcanic activity had thrust to the surface the rocks which constituted the earth's crust.

By the 1830's a synthesis of these positions had emerged. It was recognized by most geologists that both precipitation and vulcanism were important in the formation of the earth. Sedimentary rocks, such as limestone, originated in precipitation from water; igneous rocks, such as basalt and granite, were, as the vulcanists had said, thrust up from deep beneath the surface. Metamorphic rocks, the third major classification, were formed when sedimentary or igneous rocks were subjected to the heat or pressure of the earth's interior. Thus, marble was formed when a sedimentary rock, limestone, was metamorphosed by heat and pressure.[1]

No sooner had a consensus been established on the general nature of rock formation than the controversy between catastrophists and uniformitarians broke out. The catastrophists' chief spokesmen were the English geologist William Buckland and the great French anatomist and pale-

[1] Charles Coulston Gillispie, *Genesis and Geology* (Cambridge, 1951), pp. 40–97. See also, Frank Dawson Adams, *The Birth and Development of the Geological Sciences* (Baltimore, 1938), pp. 209–249.

ontologist Georges Cuvier. Buckland and Cuvier used evidence such as the abrupt breaks in the fossil record to argue that the earth was subjected to sudden catastrophic periods of destruction. The uniformitarian, Charles Lyell, responded by pointing out that the catastrophist account required causes for which there was no evidence. He asserted that this was an unreasonable position in view of the fact that existing causes, such as elevation, subsidence, and erosion, could account for all of the changes in the earth's surface.

Much more than geology was at stake in this controversy. The catastrophist account was thoroughly blended with Scriptural cosmogony. The amount of time required by the catastrophists for the formation of the earth was short enough for conventional interpretations of the Bible. Floods were recognized as a very common catastrophe, a view which suited the Biblical Deluge perfectly. The catastrophist view likewise fit the Scriptural notion of an "interventionist" God who took an active hand in world affairs.[2]

The uniformitarians, on the other hand, seemed to be defying the Bible in insisting on an extremely long history for the earth. They scoffed at the notion of a universal Deluge; they went no further than to admit the possibility of a local flood in a corner of Asia Minor. Their God was a distant God who directed His creation through uniform laws which He seldom, or never, broke. The most serious threat to orthodoxy posed by uniformitarianism was implied in the dictum of James Hutton that geology showed "no vestige of a beginning,—no prospect of an end." This cyclical or nonprogressionist outlook contained a major challenge to those who insisted that nature show the designing hand of Providence.[3]

[2] Gillispie, *Genesis and Geology,* pp. 98–120.
[3] *Ibid.,* pp. 121–148.

By the 1840's scientific opinion was leaning strongly towards Lyell and his supporters. Natural theology was not far behind. Once the shock of having to adjust to scientific developments had worn off, religiously inclined scientists, like the Scottish editor and part-time geologist, Hugh Miller, soon realized that uniformitarianism held much promise for orthodoxy. Miller recognized that the God of the Free Church of Scotland was also a distant God who could not be expected to interfere regularly in the operation of the world. Constant intervention spoke poorly of God's foreknowledge. Uniformitarianism, for Miller, was geological confirmation of God's power and omniscience.

Miller also used his knowledge of paleontology to recapture the notion of design in nature. He rejected the non-progressionist aspect of uniformitarianism and insisted that paleontology, through its intricate fossil sequences, had shown once and for all that there was direction in nature.[4]

It was at this point that Dawson entered the nineteenth-century controversies. He was too young to have taken part in either the neptunist-vulcanist or uniformitarian-catastrophist clashes. However, he was just beginning his career as a geologist when Hugh Miller published *Footprints of the Creator* in 1847; in fact, he was studying in Edinburgh when the book appeared. He became principal of McGill in 1855 only two years before the publication of Miller's *The Testimony of the Rocks.* In 1860 Dawson offered his own synthesis of Scripture and the new geology in *Archaia.* He grappled with the problems raised by uniformitarianism much as Hugh Miller had. He described himself as a "modified uniformitarian," a position which included a sufficient degree of catastrophism to suit Scripture and just enough progress to admit design into nature.

[4] *Ibid.,* pp. 179–181.

Dawson was also an active participant in still another geological controversy that began in the 1830's, the debate over Louis Agassiz's hypothesis of a recent ice age. Agassiz had spent the summer of 1836 studying the Diablerets glacier in the Alps and had concluded that the erratic "drift" boulders scattered over most of Europe had been carried by glaciers much greater in volume than those then existing in the Alps. Agassiz believed that the glaciers were so extensive that the entire climate of Europe had been affected, producing the ice age.[5] This controversy had an indirect link to the two earlier geological disputes of the century, since to affirm Agassiz's hypothesis was to deny the older theory of water-borne ice as the carrier of drift and the older theory coincided very well with neptunism and the Biblical Deluge. Glaciers also accomplished their work by slow, inching movement over hundreds of years. Consequently, although Agassiz himself interpreted the ice age as a catastrophe, many catastrophists preferred the notion of a surge of water and ice which scattered the drift in a relatively short time.

Agassiz received a very cool reception at first. His ideas were advanced in Great Britain by Edward Forbes and William Buckland; the latter also interpreted glaciers in catastrophist terms. The glacial hypothesis was not widely held until the early 1860's when T. F. Jamieson and Archibald Geikie convincingly explained the glacial phenomena of England on the basis of the glacier theory.

One of the British geologists who received Agassiz coolly was Charles Lyell. Lyell was impressed by the present effects of water-borne ice on the rocky shores of Scotland and, on the uniformitarian principle, found it more credible to propose floating ice as the cause of the drift in most of the

[5] Richard Foster Flint, *Glacial Geology and the Pleistocene Epoch* (New York, 1947), pp. 2–6; J. K. Charlesworth, *The Quaternary Era* (London, 1957) 2: pp. 614–633.

British Isles. Lyell accepted Agassiz's views of the glaciation of the Highlands. Dawson followed Lyell in this, partly because of the latter's great personal influence on him and partly because of his own experience with the drift ice of the Nova Scotia coast. Dawson published his own views on glacial matters in *Acadian Geology* in 1855. He claimed that North America provided the best evidence of the inadequacy of the glacial hypothesis. This was a position he advanced untiringly until his death in 1899, despite a definite shift in scientific opinion which, after 1865, tended more and more to favor glaciation as the source of drift.

In addition to these contentious geological issues, Dawson was involved in two other major controversies, the polygenism dispute and the protracted debate over evolution. The first of these, the polygenism dispute, reflected a perennial interest in the origin of the human race. This interest was given a sharper focus in 1839, when Samuel Morton, an American physician, published *Crania Americana.* Morton made use of an extensive collection of human skulls to raise the question of the multiplicity of the human species. Without taking a clear position on this question, Morton produced strong evidence that the differences between the crania of the various races were so extensive that classification of the several races as one species was very doubtful.[6] In 1844 Morton wrote *Crania Aegyptiaca,* a study of newly discovered skulls from the tombs of Egypt. The results of this study showed, he said, that the same degree of difference had existed four thousand years ago.

*Crania Aegyptiaca* brought matters to a climax. Only two conclusions could be drawn from Morton's book: either the races of man were variations of one species, in which case the insignificant changes since the Pharoahs implied

[6] William Stanton, *The Leopard's Spots* (Chicago, 1960), pp. 25–35.

that man had been created much longer ago than seemed accountable in Scripture, or several separate species had been created relatively recently, i.e., within the conventional six-thousand-year period.[7] Four years later, in 1848, Ephraim G. Squier's *Ancient Monuments of the Mississippi Valley* provided a similar dilemma with indigenous materials.[8]

The polygenist conclusion was reflected in the work of two of Morton's followers, Josiah Nott and George Gliddon, who collaborated on *Types of Mankind* in 1855 and *Indigenous Races of the Earth* in 1857. Nott and Gliddon made the forthright judgments which Morton had avoided. Nott, a physician in Mobile, Alabama, made the link between polygenism and the slave society of the South, and claimed that the allegedly smaller crania of African races were scientific proof of Negro inferiority. Nott, Gliddon, Morton, and Squier formed the nucleus of what became known as the "American School" of anthropology. The identifying marks of the "American School" were polygenism and a belief that the American Indians did not belong to the Mongolian race but constituted, rather, a separate race and species.[9]

Dawson was opposed to both of these views, especially polygenism. Nearly half of his second book, *Archaia,* was devoted to a vigorous assertion of the traditional monogenist position. Dawson's response to the "American School" was to emphasize the great capacity of the human race to vary and to migrate. Along with other monogenists, such as John Bachman, Asa Gray, and James Dwight Dana, Dawson made much of the interfertility of the human races; this interfertility showed, he contended, that all races belonged to one species. Ironically, the greatest boost to

[7] *Ibid.,* pp. 49–53.
[8] *Ibid.,* pp. 82–89.
[9] *Ibid.,* pp. 162–168, 175–180.

the arguments of monogenist defenders of scientific and Scriptural orthodoxy came from Charles Darwin. *The Origin of Species* was filled with evidence of the ability of one species to vary in the manner proposed for the human race by the monogenists.

It was often the fate of the embattled defenders of nineteenth-century orthodoxy to find that the solution to one of their problems contained still greater difficulties. Such was the case with Darwin and monogenism. Dawson himself attempted unsuccessfully to accept Darwin's views on variation, while denying that they could be extended to speciation. The intensity of the furor that raged over evolution overshadowed almost completely the debates over vulcanism, uniformitarianism, glaciers, and polygenism.

The idea of evolution was already old when the famous papers of Darwin and Alfred Russel Wallace were read in 1858. The French biologist, Jean Baptiste de Lamarck, stirred considerable discussion with his *Philosophie Zoologique* in 1809. Lamarck noted that the active use of particular faculties tended to develop these faculties and that disuse caused atrophy, the precisely opposite effect. He believed that the results of use or disuse in a parent were passed on to offspring, i.e., that acquired characteristics were inheritable. The combination of these principles led Lamarck to propose a theory of evolution: organisms could change indefinitely through use and disuse, while the inheritance of acquired characteristics provided a mechanism for combining the small alterations in each generation into changes significant enough to mark a new species. In 1844 Lamarck's ideas were presented in a very aggressive form by the English journalist and publisher, Robert Chambers. Writing anonymously, for reasons of discretion, Chambers published *Vestiges of the Natural History of Creation,* an attempt to correlate Lamarck's ideas with new discoveries in paleontology. The scientific community was almost unanimous in rejecting Chambers's book. Thomas H. Huxley, later to earn the title "Darwin's bulldog" for his ferocious defense of evolution, led the attack. Chambers opened the subject of evolution to a wider audience and actually began the public controversy that characterized Darwin's reception fifteen years later. As Loren Eiseley wrote in *Darwin's Century,* Chambers "first drew the lightning." [10]

Although *Vestiges of the Natural History of Creation* came under fire largely for scientific reasons, a grave threat to orthodoxy was contained in the theories of Lamarck and Chambers. Did not the Bible clearly state that a species reproduced "after his kind"? It was a matter of elementary logic to deduce that the evolutionists' views implied that at some point species did not reproduce as the Bible indicated.

The Lamarckian outlook at least preserved design, for it could always be said that God had given His creatures the capacity to evolve through use and disuse and the inheritance of acquired characteristics. For many, even this small consolation was removed when Darwin published *The Origin of Species* in 1859. Some, such as Alfred Russel Wallace and Asa Gray, were able to see design working through natural selection; others, such as Louis Agassiz and Dawson, regarded natural selection as a contradiction in terms and saw no hope of salvaging the Providence of God in a "nature red in tooth and claw." [11]

With the exception of the disputes over vulcanism and uniformitarianism, Dawson was actively engaged in all of these controversies. Since they were crucial to most of nineteenth-century geology and biology, Dawson's participation in these controversies brought him attention he would not otherwise have received. His only other important controversy was over a topic of much less magnitude,

[10] Loren Eiseley, *Darwin's Century* (Garden City, N. Y., 1958), pp. 135–140.
[11] *Ibid.,* pp. 193–203.

the organic nature of *Eozoön canadense;* nevertheless, this controversy, too, brought Dawson considerable notoriety.

*Eozoön* had been found in 1858 in the Precambrian rocks of the Ottawa valley. The coral-like surface of untreated specimens of *Eozoön* immediately suggested to Sir William Logan, the director of the Geological Survey of Canada, that it might be a fossil. Prepared specimens looked to the layman very much like a piece of green and white marble. The practiced eye of Logan, however, noticed a regular alternation of green and white layers which also indicated that *Eozoön* was organic in origin. Although the individual cell of *Eozoön* was microscopic in size, it was found in huge sheets which suggested to several observers that it had lived in colonies and had been a reef builder.

Since, if authentic, *Eozoön* antedated considerably any fossils known at that time, it was a very important discovery. When *Eozoön* was brought to him for microscope analysis, Dawson declared that it was a foraminifer much more complex and many times larger than any hitherto found.[12] Dawson's advocacy of *Eozoön* as a foraminifer aroused almost immediate opposition. A number of articulate skeptics believed that *Eozoön* was simply an unusually regular inorganic form. Although this view was eventually proved correct, paleontologists generally accepted *Eozoön* as organic, especially in the early decades of the controversy.

The declaration that *Eozoön* was a foraminifer made the discovery even more important and brought the dispute over its organic nature into other controversies. The presence of an animal such as *Eozoön* in the oldest rocks of the earth's crust required new explanations of the Biblical order of creation, since Genesis explicitly stated that plants

[12] George P .Merrill, *The First One Hundred Years of American Geology* (New Haven, 1924), pp. 564–579.

were created on the third day, while animals were not created until the fifth day. Furthermore, *Eozoön* was separated by a stupendous time gap from any related form and, therefore, was very significant in the debate over evolution. If Dawson's opinion that it was a gigantic foraminifer were correct, evolutionists would have had to contend not only with an immense gap in time and in the paleontological record, but also with the presence of a very advanced and complex form preceding in time much simpler Foraminifera.

Dawson's involvement in the *Eozoön* discussion was inevitable, since in the 1860's he was the only accomplished microscopist in Canada and specimens of *Eozoön* were as a matter of course brought to him for investigation. Once he became aware of the dramatic possibilities *Eozoön* offered in combatting evolution, he was determined to exploit them to the fullest. A similar motivation was responsible for Dawson's entry into his other controversies. As with *Eozoön,* he continually sought to extend the results of original research on Canadian materials to the larger issues of the day. For example, he used observations of the effects of floating ice in the St. Lawrence to oppose the glacial hypothesis. He employed his intensive knowledge of Canadian fossils to counter the evolutionists. He concocted ingenious arguments to show that the culture of the Canadian Indians proved the correctness of the human chronology found in Scripture. The key to Dawson's career as a controversialist was his use of Canadian materials to enter the mainstream of nineteenth-century controversy.

The sequence of the following chapters on Dawson's role in these controversies is, to some extent, arbitrary. Except for a few perfunctory pages in which he attributed the glacial phenomena of Nova Scotia to floating ice, Dawson did not engage actively in any of these issues until 1860. On the other hand, by 1865, he was thoroughly involved in all of them and, without exception, he wrote on these issues until his death. It is very difficult, therefore, to arrange Dawson's career as a controversialist in a neat chronological order. The sequence which follows is based on the order in which these controversies occupied the major part of Dawson's attention.

With four of these disputes, this rough chronological order follows a rational topical order as well. The dispute over geology and Genesis naturally led to the work of the sixth day, the creation of man; this in turn led to a discussion of the unity of man. Since the capacity of species to vary was crucial to the polygenism debate, evolution logically followed polygenism. Dawson began work on *Eozoön* only because he was asked to examine some specimens. However, his role in the controversy over its organic origin was due, in large measure, to his interest in evolution. The glacier question alone does not fit this rational order. It had only a tenuous logical connection to Dawson's other controversies. Simply chronologically, his thorough involvement in this dispute followed his entry into the other four issues. Similarly, his last major book, *The Canadian Ice Age,* was devoted to this controversy. For these reasons, this chapter is placed last.

# *III. The Word and the Work*

THE FIRST HALF of the nineteenth century was a period of great achievement in geology; this was the "heroic age" which provided the foundation for geology as we know it. It was an age in which Murchison, Sedgwick, de la Beche, Jameson, Phillips, and Lyell, just to name a few, trudged on foot over the British Isles and recorded their original observations.

The flood of data accumulated in these years revolutionized geology, while the impact on the related field of Biblical exegesis was immense. Never was the "marvelous flexibility" of the Hebrew language more thoroughly tested. The fact that the first half of the nineteenth century was also a period that combined William Paley's providential natural theology with renewed Evangelical interest in Scripture made the search for synthesis even more acute. Providentialism, Evangelicalism, and scientific discovery were a volatile combination.[1]

Since William Dawson was a geologist who was both a Providentialist and an Evangelical, he personally embodied this volatile combination. It was not surprising, therefore, that he maintained an enthusiastic interest in the geology-Genesis discussion. As a young man Dawson was an avid reader of religio-scientific syntheses such as the Bridgewater Treatises. He was especially drawn to the work of Thomas Chalmers, Pye Smith, and Hugh Miller, but he rejected the work of the American exegete, Edward Hitchcock.

It was Miller who most appealed to Dawson. Miller's first book, *The Old Red Sandstone,* had been published in Edinburgh in 1841, while Dawson was a student there.

[1] Charles Coulston Gillispie, *Genesis and Geology* (Cambridge, 1951), pp. 6–8.

The young Nova Scotian was attracted from the first by Miller's persuasive pen and was much influenced by his subsequent work, *The Footprints of the Creator* (1847) and *The Testimony of the Rocks* (1857).

Miller offered a balanced approach to the relation of science and Scripture. He was a very well-informed scientist and his work had none of the obscurantism or narrow literalism that characterized many natural theologies.[2] Miller's work, like Paley's, accomplished a *tour de force* in using scientific ideas with anti-orthodox implications to buttress orthodox Christianity. Miller's books were the first widely read and accepted syntheses of science and Scripture to be based wholly on the uniformitarian outlook. Uniformitarianism contained several threats to orthodoxy. The notion that existing causes accounted for all of the details of the earth's surface undermined the providentialism of Scripture. A similar challenge was raised by uniformitarian geology to the six days of creation and the Biblical Flood.

Miller offered the great advantage of synthesizing Scripture with the most advanced science of the day. For example, when Miller wrote his famous *The Footprints of the Creator* to refute Robert Chambers's *Vestiges of the Natural History of Creation,* the general scientific opinion was that Miller had used sound, empirical science to strike down pretentious quackery. Miller's technique was to apply his intimate knowledge of the Old Red Sandstone[3] to the evolutionary hypothesis advanced by Chambers. The result was a triumph for Miller. Evolution, as proposed by Chambers, simply could not account for the presence of a highly developed fish, the *Asterolepis,* as far back as the Old Red Sandstone.[4]

[2] *Ibid.,* pp. 163, 247.

[3] A rock formation deposited during the Devonian period.

[4] Gillispie, *Genesis and Geology,* pp. 162, 174–175.

In 1857 Miller turned his attention from rebuttal of Chambers and intensive analysis of one geological period to the broader question of Biblical and scientific cosmogony. Although his reception by most scientists was less warm, his appeal to Dawson was undiminished. Dawson reviewed *The Testimony of the Rocks* for a Canadian scientific journal and gave it the highest praise. Miller's work was "the best guide to the reconciliation" of science and Scripture, in Dawson's opinion.[5]

Miller's reconciliation rested on three main principles. The first of these was, even by 1857, a traditional one; the "days" of Genesis were long periods of time, creative days, not solar days. The second principle was that Moses's account was based on a vision, a sort of tableau, that God stretched before Moses's eyes. Moses then simply recorded the phenomena he observed. This, said Miller, explained the preeminently visual character of Genesis and the fact that, from a scientific point of view, Moses's account left much unsaid. The vision was inspired but Moses's eyes were not; consequently, he recorded only those details that would strike the untutored layman as most meaningful. Miller's third principle extended the notion of the "untutored observer" from observations of the vision to observations of nature itself. Thus, passages in the Bible such as those which implied a geocentric universe or spoke of a "firmament" represented a faithful record of direct observations. This interpretation, said Miller, did violence to neither science nor Scripture; the prophets of old called them as they saw them and, for that matter, to the unaided eye the sky still looks like a solid blue bowl.

Accordingly to his first principle, Miller held that the "days" of Genesis should be construed as long periods, al-

[5] J. William Dawson in *The Canadian Naturalist and Geologist* 2 (May, 1857): p. 87.

though he believed that from a geological point of view only three of these periods were significant. The first was the third day of Genesis in which plants were created; this, in Miller's view, corresponded closely with the Paleozoic Era of geology and, more specifically, with the Carboniferous period. The second geologically significant period was the fifth day of Genesis, when God created "creeping things." The fifth day, for Miller, corresponded with the Secondary (or Mesozoic) Era of geology, the so-called Age of Reptiles and Age of Birds. His third period was the sixth day, the day in which mammals, including man, were created; this, he said, corresponded to the Tertiary (or Cenozoic) Era of geology.[6]

This correspondence between revealed theology and natural theology was, to say the least, general, as Miller readily admitted. This generality, he contended, was due not to any inherent incompatibility of the two theologies but, rather, to the general nature of revelation. The vision granted to Moses was primarily for a moral purpose and was relevant for the scientist only in so far as it contained no error and, on the positive side, presented the great typical forms of each Era. Hence, when primitive mammals were found in the Mesozoic Era, Scriptural accuracy was unaffected because no scientist would argue that mammals were typical of the Mesozoic.[7]

Miller, therefore, saw geology as in no sense opposed to a natural theology based on Scripture. When properly interpreted the new knowledge of the earth's crust tended to confirm the Scriptural account:

> It has been said that the inferences of the geologist militate against those of the theologian. Nay, not those of our higher geologists and higher theologians,—not what our Murchisons and

[6] Hugh Miller, *The Testimony of the Rocks* (New York, 1857), pp. 158–160, 196–204.

[7] *Ibid.*, p. 192.

Sedgwicks infer in one field, with what our Chalmerses and Isaac Taylors infer in the other. Between the Word and the Works of God there can be no actual discrepancies.[8]

For Miller, geology was an extension of Paley's thought. Where Paley made the deist outlook and deist science work for orthodox Christianity, Miller did the same for the new geology. Where Paley found an intricately contrived clock lying in a field and from it inferred a clockmaker and so on back to that Great Clockmaker, Miller went a step further—beyond philosophic inference to geological fact.[9]

The notion of scientific proof of revelation was especially attractive to the evangelically minded Dawson. He believed that the Bible had never opposed true science and that Hugh Miller had shown that one complemented the other. When he entered the fray with the publication of *Archaia* in 1860, Dawson took great pains to establish that the warfare of the past had been due to conflict between science and pseudo-Scriptural Christianity. "Exhumed from the rubbish of the middle ages," the Bible "has entered on a new career of victory." [10] The whole question of the relation of science to religion was "at the present moment in a more satisfactory state than ever previously." [11] Those scientists who denigrated the Bible were ignoring its beneficial influence and confusing obscurantist religious practices with Scripture itself.

The Bible was Good News for science as well as for religion, in Dawson's opinion. The notion of uniform cause in nature, arrived at by science only recently and after long and hard work, was evident in Genesis and continued throughout the Bible. The Old Testament was good science, as far as Dawson was concerned; it had been

[8] *Ibid.*, p. 280.
[9] *Ibid.*, pp. 211–212.
[10] J. William Dawson, *Archaia* (Montreal, 1860), p. 11.
[11] *Ibid.*, p. 17.

either unknown or neglected successively by pagan Greece and Rome, the Roman Catholic Church and, now, by some modern scientists who erred "not knowing the Scriptures." [12]

Dawson was not even willing to go as far as Miller in explaining the geocentricism of the Old Testament. Where Miller used the principle of untutored observation, Dawson pointed an accusing finger at Greek polytheism and medieval barbarism. These two dark ages added their own superstitious accretions to the original Hebrew texts. Thus, according to Dawson, geocentricism was found in the Septuagint, but not in the Hebrew original.[13] This position, extended to other thorny exegetical problems, made it possible for him to claim a close affinity between modern science and the science of "the golden age of primeval monotheism." [14]

This alleged affinity, in its turn, caused some additional problems for Dawson. He was placed in a very difficult position in dealing with texts of unquestioned Hebrew authenticity. He was forced to show direct affinity where other writers could use a metonymic or mytho-poetic approach. Where Hugh Miller urged a metonymic approach to the order of creation, Dawson had to be much more specific. More particularly, Dawson could not accept the quasi-literal view of Edward Hitchcock.

Hitchcock, a Congregationalist minister and President of Amherst College who was also a professional geologist, had published a widely read synthetic study, *The Religion*

[12] *Ibid.*, pp. 19–21.

[13] *Ibid.*, pp. 44–45. Dawson gave no source for this fanciful position; neither did he note specific recensions from the Hebrew text. He probably derived his opinion from John Kitto (1804–1854) who held a position very close to this. Kitto was a popular English Biblicist whose work was often referred to by Dawson. See for example, Kitto's *An Illustrated History of the Bible* (Norwich, Conn., 1870), p. 458.

[14] Dawson, *Archaia*, p. 48.

*of Geology,* in 1851.[15] Hitchcock, too, believed that the record of the rocks vindicated the Biblical cosmogony and in some ways he was more of a literalist than Dawson. However, Hitchcock's method of reconciliation was fundamentally unacceptable to Dawson, and the two chief motivations for Dawson's entry into the geology-Genesis controversy lay in his objections to Hitchcock and Miller. First, despite the fact that he was an avid admirer of Hugh Miller, he found fault with *The Testimony of the Rocks* on several key points. More important, Dawson found Hitchcock's influential book to be unsound in principle.

An additional factor, which will be treated in a subsequent chapter, was the recent development of the "American School" of anthropology and ethnology. The traditional Scriptural view of the unity of man had been effectively challenged by "the American School." The polygenism of Louis Agassiz was especially offensive to Dawson and a large portion of the latter's *Archaia* consisted of a lengthy attack on Agassiz's position.[16] In short, Dawson's entry into the discussion was primarily in rebuttal to the views of the Americans.

Dawson began his rebuttal, appropriately enough, with Genesis I: 1: "In the beginning God created the heaven and the earth."[17] The word used for "created" in the authentic Hebrew text, said Dawson, was *bara,* which meant absolute creation or creation from nothing. He thought it most significant that the word was used very infrequently in the Bible: a few times in a clearly literary sense, once (in Genesis I: 1) for the creation of the inorganic world, and once for the creation of man.[18] The word

15 Edward Hitchcock, *The Religion of Geology* (Boston, 1851).

16 For a concise statement of Agassiz's racial views, see William Stanton, *The Leopard's Spots* (Chicago, 1960), pp. 100–109.

17 Since this was the translation used by Dawson, Scriptural quotations in this study are taken from the Authorized King James Version.

18 Dawson, *Archaia,* pp. 61–63.

*bara,* then, properly understood, implied the direct intervention of God. Since subsequent verses of Genesis I used phrases such as "Let there be light" (Genesis I: 3), "Let there be a firmament" (Genesis I: 6), "Let the earth bring forth" (Genesis I: 9), Dawson argued that the author of Genesis was making a clear distinction between direct and mediate creation.[19]

This much was in no way exceptional; both Miller and Hitchcock, for example, followed the same exegetical path. Dawson's agreement with Hitchcock, however, lasted for only one verse. Hitchcock maintained that there was no reason to assume that the events of Genesis I: 2 were consecutive to those of the first verse. In his view, it was likely that the second and following verses referred to events far removed from "the beginning." In fact, Hitchcock saw the entire six days of creation as merely the final rearranging of a universe that was put in order in the vast period of time that elapsed between "the beginning" and these changes introduced, from a geologist's point of view, very recently.[20] Within this limited framework, Hitchcock accepted Hugh Miller's "visual revelation" as opposed to Dawson's "verbal revelation."

Hitchcock went even further and adopted the position of the English exegete, Pye Smith, that after the first verse "earth" in Genesis did not refer to the entire globe but only to a portion of Asia Minor. For Hitchcock, this view had the advantage of explaining distribution of animals (already a vexing question in 1851) without miracle, since it allowed for the unrevealed creation of species elsewhere on the earth. Hitchcock also believed in a very limited Flood, a Flood that was universal only from Noah's vantage point on the deck of the Ark. Consequently, the unrevealed creation was not affected by the Flood and the

19 *Ibid.,* pp. 160–162.
20 Hitchcock, *The Religion of Geology,* pp. 38–39.

undeniable survival of some species from remotest time could likewise be explained without miracle.[21]

Although Dawson found much to praise in Hitchcock's views, notably in his treatment of the Flood, the basic outlook of *The Religion of Geology* was unacceptable to him: "Truth obliges us . . . to confess that both geology and scripture refuse to be reconciled on this basis." [22] Dawson maintained that it was clear that "earth" in Genesis I: 1 signified "whole globe"; it was, therefore, unreasonable to assume that the same word would have a different meaning in the very next verse. This was especially evident since Genesis I: 10 ("And God called the dry land earth") explicitly limited the meaning of "earth" to a portion of the globe. It was a gross violation of the elementary principles of exegesis, in Dawson's opinion, to presume an unstated but much greater limitation on the meaning of "earth" in Genesis I: 2, when the same writer took the trouble to specify a limitation in Genesis I: 10.[23]

Dawson thought that the gap posited by Hitchcock between the first and second verses of Genesis was equally unreasonable. The alleged gap, practically speaking, lay in the pre-geological past of the earth and in such an area it was as difficult to disprove as it was to prove.

> Geology, as a science of observation and induction, does not carry us back to this period. It must still and always say, with Hutton, that it can find no trace of a beginning, no prospect of an end.[24]

However, according to Dawson, some facts were available on the "pre-geological" condition of the earth. These facts, he said, pointed toward a very different position from that advanced by Hitchcock.

[21] *Ibid.*, pp. 61–62.
[22] Dawson, *Archaia*, p. 75.
[23] *Ibid.*, pp. 72–75.
[24] *Ibid.*, p .83.

The facts that Dawson had in mind were those that were used to support the nebular hypothesis of the origin of the universe. The nebular hypothesis, much in vogue in 1860, was proposed by the great German philosopher, Immanuel Kant, and was presented in its most widely accepted form by Pierre Simon de La Place, a noted French mathematician; the theory is often referred to as simply "the La Placean hypothesis." According to La Place, our solar system probably began in a hot vaporous mass that rotated in one direction around a central nucleus that was more dense than the rest of the mass; the gravitational attraction of the denser nucleus kept the mass moving in a regular path around it. As this mass cooled it began to solidify into particles which continued rotating around the nucleus; the larger particles began to exert a small gravitational pull of their own. The gravitational pull of these particles then attracted other smaller particles; the cycle of accretion of larger mass and resulting greater gravitational attraction eventually terminated in the formation of the planets, while the original nucleus, not yet completely cooled, became the sun.

Although it is no longer accepted by scientists, La Place's hypothesis had much to recommend it. The hypothesis accounted admirably for the nearly circular orbits of the planets, for their rotation in one direction around the sun and in one direction on their own axes. The theory also explained the rotation of the planets on a plane very close to the sun's equator. The clinching evidence, for proponents of the theory, was the condition of Saturn; with existent rings near its equator, Saturn was thought to be incompletely developed, an example of the condition that had previously existed for other planets. The ringed planet provided La Place with a measure of empirical evidence that was very persuasive in the nineteenth century.

The nebular hypothesis was very important for Dawson in his synthesis of Scripture and science. It was especially useful in combatting Hitchcock's proposal of a gap in time between the first and second verses of Genesis and the proposal's exegetical corollaries. For Dawson, the relation between the account of Genesis and the sequence of events posited by La Place was almost exact. Both indicated that the raw materials of the universe were created before the heavens and the earth assumed their distinct forms. The condensing nebular mass was in accord with the Scriptural "deep." The troublesome question of the origin of light (in Genesis I: 3) before the creation of the sun or other luminaries (in Genesis I: 14–18) was perfectly explained by the nebular theory. The vaporous particles produced both light and heat as they condensed but it was only after they had condensed into a roughly globular and solid condition that it was possible to call the sun a luminary in any special sense or to refer to a separation of night from day.[25] Dawson, therefore, argued that there was no good reason to accept the "gap." On the positive side, opposed to the pure speculation of Hitchcock and Pye Smith, there was Saturn, a laboratory specimen, preserved for all to see.

The major corollary of Hitchcock's "gap in time" view, a rather liberal position, was a curiously literal interpretation of "day" in Genesis. There was no compelling reason, either theological or geological, for Hitchcock to take this position. The chief motivation seemed to be a sense of disproportion between the omnipotence of God and the small amount of work that Hitchcock left for God to do in the six days of Genesis. This disproportion, in effect, turned the tables and made it theologically unreasonable to presume the long periods of time of many interpreters.

Dawson was one of these interpreters and, since he was committed to a verbal inspiration, the actual words of

[25] Dawson, *Archaia*, pp. 84–85, 89.

Genesis and their exact meaning were crucial to him. Although his position was generally much more literal, he took issue with Hitchcock on the meaning of "day." He regarded the point as "far from being settled," but he had some very definite opinions. The word "day" (*yom* in Hebrew) occurred twice in Genesis I: 5, the verse in which it first appeared:

And God called the light Day; and the darkness he called Night. And the evening and the morning were the first day.

Dawson's approach to the problem posed by these conflicting usages was to attempt to show that the very aspect of the problem that was most difficult, when properly understood, contributed most to Dawson's own position. This had also been his technique in applying the nebular hypothesis to the "light before luminaries" question.

Dawson extended this attempt to make difficulties work in his favor to the usage of *yom* in Genesis I: 5. Thus, the author of Genesis used *yom* in two different senses precisely to indicate "that *the day of creation is not the day of popular speech*" [Italics Dawson's].[26] Dawson argued that the Hebrew word *yom* usually signified only the "natural day" or daylight hours. When a twenty-four-hour cycle of night and day was meant, Scripture usually contained another expression, a compound phrase such as "day and night." Therefore, it was unlikely that *yom* in Genesis I: 5 stood for a twenty-four-hour period. On the other hand the twelve-hour period (*yom* as "daylight hours") was specifically excluded by the phrase "the evening and the morning were the first day." Dawson concluded from this Scholastic-like examination that there was a strong presumption in favor of the view that *yom*, neither twelve nor twenty-four hours, signified a long period of time.[27] Further, indirect, evidence of this view, according to Dawson,

[26] *Ibid.*, p. 100.
[27] *Ibid.*, p. 101.

was the common use of *yom* in this sense in other parts of the Bible.[28]

The marvelous flexibility of *yom* was not the only aspect of the Scriptural "days" that concerned Dawson in his attack on Hitchcock. Hitchcock argued that the absence of rain until the third day was "altogether probable if the days were of twenty-four hours but absurd if they were longer periods." [29] Equally absurd was the creation of plants before it rained. For Dawson, "the absurdity here is all on the side of the short days." [30] If the days of creation were only twenty-four hours in duration, two days without rain would have been so normal that it would have been unreasonable even to mention the fact in an account that was otherwise very meager in such details. Dawson's position was that the first two "days" involved the initial formation and clearing up of the atmosphere; therefore, conditions were such that rain as we know it could not have formed. He envisaged the earth in a misty, vaporous state, a state which coincided nicely with both the nebular hypothesis and Genesis II: 6: "There went up a mist from the earth, and watered the whole face of the ground." Here again he attempted to make the very difficulty work on his behalf; it was entirely probable, he said, that rain did not fall, while at the same time conditions were excellent for plant life. Conditions, in fact, resembled those of a hothouse.[31]

To support his view that the six days of Genesis were concerned with recent arrangements, Hitchcock had pointed out that paleontology had shown that the oldest

[28] *Ibid.*, pp. 103–105. A few of the examples cited by Dawson were: Genesis 11: 4 "In the day when Jehovah Elohim made the earth and the heaven" in which the context indicated that *yom* meant all six days of creation; Job 18: 20 "They that come after him shall be astonished at his day"; Judges 18: 30 "he and his sons were priests to the tribe of Dan until the day of the captivity of the land"; 2 Peter 3: 8 "One day is with the Lord as a thousand years."

[29] Hitchcock, *Religion of Geology*, p. 65.

[30] Dawson, *Archaia*, p. 115.

[31] *Ibid.*, pp. 164–165.

fossils were animal, yet the Bible stated clearly that plants were created first. Dawson replied that paleontology went back only to the fifth and sixth days of creation; hence, the plant creation and the great physical changes of the fourth day were all contained in the metamorphosed rocks that were then called Azoic (i.e., lifeless).[32] Hitchcock had implied that only two alternatives were possible: either the Scriptural cosmogony referred to recent events or the paleontological record plainly contradicted Scripture. For Hitchcock the findings of paleontology were either irrelevant or irreconcilable.

Dawson proposed a third alternative: the plant creation of the third day had been destroyed during the changes of the fourth day and, consequently, the Paleozoic animals represented the fifth day of creation. The great achievement of modern geology, in Dawson's opinion, had been to expose the prejudice that the history of the earth was coextensive with human history. He chided Hitchcock for substituting another prejudice, the dogma that the history of the earth equalled geological history.[33]

This position led Dawson to reject a major postulate of Hugh Miller that the third day was roughly equivalent to the Carboniferous period of geology. Dawson drew support for this rejection from the fact that marks left by raindrops were clearly preserved in Devonian rocks (pre-Carboniferous); hence, rain "as at present" fell before Miller's third day, yet Genesis II: 6 explicitly stated that rain did not occur until the third day. Dawson pointed out that the best geological estimate of the first land indicated that it was neither very extensive nor very elevated. It was, therefore, probable that the temperature was uniform

[32] *Ibid.*, p. 118. The discovery of fossils and alleged fossils in these rocks soon resulted in a change in terminology. The Azoic became the Precambrian, the term in use today. Dawson, with his work on *Eozoön canadense,* was partly responsible for the discarding of "Azoic."

[33] Dawson, *Archaia,* p. 169.

and the atmosphere moist; these factors, combined with great heat from the sun and the earth itself, probably produced "gentle and continued precipitation of finely divided moisture." [34] These were, he said, ideal conditions for plants.

Although Dawson's publication was elicited by a negative reaction to Hitchcock and a desire to amend some of Hugh Miller's work, he held independent views that went beyond mere rebuttal. Dawson was concerned with the defensive posture of most synthesizers. He wanted a more definite and positive approach. The very word *reconcile* had a defensive aura and Dawson insisted on more than this. He wanted to show not only that one could reconcile geology and Genesis but, rather, that science was slowly unravelling truths that lay buried and unrecognized in the Bible.

In this vein, Dawson cited recent scientific evidence that the huge quantity of graphite found in the "Azoic" rocks was of organic origin; the graphite was indirect evidence of the creation of the third day. Dawson maintained that nineteenth-century botanical classification closely followed the order of Genesis I: 11:

> Let the earth bring forth grass, the herb yielding seed, and the fruit tree yielding fruit after his kind, whose seed is in itself.

The word translated as grass in Genesis I: 11 was *deshé,* said Dawson, and had been incorrectly translated in the King James version. The word actually meant "tender herbs" and this meaning was clearly the one intended by the author of Genesis since grass bore seed and the seed-bearing herbs were separately designated in the following phrase. An agricultural people, such as the Hebrews, would not have confused the two classes of plants. *Deshé,* then, meant in nineteenth-century terms Cryptogamia—

[34] *Ibid.*, pp. 164–165.

seedless plants such as fungi, mosses, ferns, and lichens. The "herb yielding seed" was clearly the Phanerogamia of nineteenth-century botany. Genesis I: 11, in Dawson's opinion, made a precise distinction between the two great classes of plants, a distinction that differed from nineteenth-century classification only in failing to distinguish herbaceous plants from trees.[35]

The order of creation in Genesis I: 11 was also evidence of the scientific accuracy of Scripture. A scientist who knew nothing of the Bible would expect to find organisms such as mosses and lichens antedating other plant life, since the first soil must have been highly mineralized and incapable of supporting higher forms of life. In the economy of nature, the *deshé* prepared the soil for later plants.[36] The same principle applied throughout the introduction of organic forms. Dawson cited the views of Dana and Guyot who held that the early atmosphere probably contained quantities of carbonic acid that were lethal for animals; the early plants performed the necessary function of removing the excess carbonic acid.[37]

Dawson's explanation of the order of plant creation was a good example of the Paleyism implicit in his synthesis. There was, of course, always the ironic technique, employed by Paley against the extreme deists, of using the opposition's scientific insights to defend orthodoxy. The technique was important to Dawson because it underlay his entire strategy; it was crucial on the tactical level, e.g., the "light before luminaries" and "plants before rain" issues. In discussing the order of plant creation a new, more explicit, element of Paleyism entered Dawson's account, utility. Science showed that the order in Scripture was not only true; it was useful. God was not only a Creator; He was a Contriver.

35 *Ibid.*, pp. 160–162.
36 *Ibid.*, p. 166.
37 *Ibid.*, pp. 171–172.

Contrivance was evident to Dawson in the plant creation of the third day, a period which greatly interested him. His analysis followed closely that of Hugh Miller. He disagreed strongly, however, with Miller's correlation of the third day with the Carboniferous period. In Dawson's opinion, the Carboniferous period fell within the fifth day. He thus neatly avoided the embarrassment suffered by Miller from the discovery of animal remains below the Carboniferous. As previously mentioned, Dawson's fourth day became the period of metamorphosis that destroyed the remains of the third day's vegetation and left only crystallized rocks with large graphite deposits, rocks such as those which composed Canada's Laurentian Shield with which Dawson was very familiar. Except for this chronological difference, Dawson's discussion of creation was practically the same as Miller's.

Dawson went beyond Miller, however, in attempting to reconcile the Scriptural account of Eden and the Fall with modern geology. Dawson was concerned with establishing the possibility of a place such as Eden in a world that science had shown to be full of predators. Had nature been "red in tooth and claw" in Eden, too? If not, how had the predaceous fauna revealed by paleontology lived?

Dawson's answer was that an idyllic Eden was ecologically possible, since species were usually confined to local centers. It was, therefore, likely that the site of Eden was outside of the centers of rapacious animals. These predators may simply have never occupied the territory that contained Eden, or, if they had, may have been eliminated by migration or extinction.[38] For Dawson, the cursing of the ground for man's sake consisted in God's allowing predaceous animals and plants such as the "thorns also and the thistles" of Genesis III: 18 to invade Eden. According to this ecological interpretation, Eden was a local center espe-

[38] *Ibid.*, pp. 217–218.

cially adapted for man and did not extend to the whole world.[39]

This was as far as Dawson went in *Archaia* with his synthesis of geology and the first three chapters of Genesis. The remainder of the book was devoted to reconciling the Scriptural unity and antiquity of man with the new anthropology and archaeology. This question will be treated in chapter IV.

Although *Archaia* was not widely reviewed, the few notices it received were favorable. An anonymous reviewer in *Biblioteca Sacra* praised it as a valuable book.

> The author is familiar with the whole range of his subject, and has grasped it vigorously. The discussions are conducted with fairness and ability, and written in a clear and pleasant style.

According to this reviewer, *Archaia* was distinguished by a judicious treatment of both nature and revelation.[40]

An unsigned review in the *American Journal of Science* appeared just before a notice of *The Origin of Species.* The notice of Darwin's book was very restrained: "The work deserves attention, and will, we have no doubt, meet with it." [41] The review of *Archaia* was less restrained and less prophetic. Dawson was praised for his application of the nebular hypothesis to the "light before luminaries" and "plants before rain" issues.

> These difficult points are treated with much acuteness and learning. . . . If we cannot fully agree . . . we can truly say that no one has higher claim to a respectful hearing.[42]

On a private level, Sir Charles Lyell sent his congratulations to Dawson. Lyell despaired

39 *Ibid.,* pp. 218–219.
40 *Biblioteca Sacra* 17 (April, 1860): p. 444.
41 *Amer. Jour. Science,* 2nd ser., 29 (January, 1860): pp. 146–147.
42 *Ibid.,* p. 146.

> of anyone being able to reconcile the facts of modern geology and of many other sciences with the old cosmogonies handed down to us by the unknown authors of the early chapters of Genesis.[43]

Nevertheless, he thought that Dawson had done about as well as anyone could with such a fruitless task. He had fulsome praise for Dawson's attack on Agassiz and polygenism and wrote that he "was glad it was written before Darwin's book came out." [44]

"Darwin's book" changed many things, but certainly not Dawson's opinions. One of his most pronounced characteristics was great firmness of opinion; his tenacity was both his greatest strength and his greatest weakness. He changed his mind on no major issue and the synthesis of science and Scripture outlined in *Archaia* was no exception; nearly forty years later Dawson was offering the same arguments. In the intervening period he produced several books and more than a dozen articles that restated in one way or another the same point of view, which remained basically that of Hugh Miller with minor modifications where Dawson disagreed with Miller or where he was forced to accommodate new discoveries.

These modifications consisted largely of extensions of the positions in *Archaia.* For example, Dawson never accommodated his synthesis to evolution, simply because he adamantly refused to admit the mutability of species. In fact, on a tactical level, Dawson was able, after a fashion, to fit the Darwinian arguments for the unity of man into his attack on polygenism.[45] The nebular hypothesis, the great pinion of the Miller-Dawson cosmogony, was in nearly as good repute when Dawson died as it was in 1860. Thus, Dawson's subsequent publication showed relatively minor adjustments and were, for the most part, lengthy additions to his earlier ideas.

[43] Lyell to Dawson, May 15, 1860, Dawson papers.
[44] *Ibid.*
[45] See below, pp. 70–72, 74, 83–84.

Dawson's discussion of Eden and the Fall, for example, was extended in *The Origin of the World According to Revelation and Science.* In *Archaia* he had posited a local center of creation with an idyllic ecological balance. Now, in 1877, he argued that God's plan for Eden had been for this ecological balance gradually to replace the rapacious conditions of the rest of the world. As extinction eliminated predaceous fauna and inimical flora, the Edenic balance would have spread. The Fall simply resulted in a reversal of the process; the predators and thistles encroached on Eden.[46]

In an article for *The Princeton Review* published in 1879, Dawson became more specific. It was a geological commonplace, he noted, that the end of the Tertiary Era, the period of man's creation, was marked by a sharp deterioration of climate. In the mid-Tertiary semitropical plants flourished as far north as Spitzbergen; after the deterioration of climate, ice and snow covered previously temperate areas. This, said Dawson, was the "cursing of the ground" in a general sense, just as the encroachment of hostile nature was the specific curse on Eden itself.[47]

The subject was interesting enough for Dawson to devote an entire book to it in 1895. Most of *Eden Lost and Won* was a lengthy extrapolation of the earlier notions. The center of man's origin had come under much strictly scientific scrutiny in the 1880's and 1890's and it was with ill-restrained glee that Dawson cited such antagonists as Haeckel in defense of the general site designated in Genesis.[48] With his predilection for attempting to turn weaknesses into strengths, Dawson maintained that the general nature of the designation in Genesis was evidence of the

[46] J. W. Dawson, *The Origin of the World According to Revelation and Science* (New York, 1877), pp. 238–239.

[47] J. W. Dawson, "Points of Contact Between Science and Revelation," *Princeton Rev.* 57 (November, 1879), p. 584.

[48] J. W. Dawson, *Eden Lost and Won* (London, 1895), pp. 68–69.

authenticity of the Biblical account. His position was that the author of Genesis clearly knew that Eden had been largely submerged or had become a swamp because of a deluge (probably The Deluge). The author of Genesis had, therefore, refrained from specifying the precise spot. Yet, the fact that the account located Eden unmistakably, though generally, proved its authenticity.[49] In addition to this unconvincing argument, by 1895 Dawson had refined his thinking on the "thorns and thistles"; they were literal, he said, probably a layman's description of the family *Compositae* which was scarcely evident before man.[50]

The consequences of the expulsion from Eden were also of interest to Dawson. Since he believed firmly in the stability of species, especially *Homo sapiens,* the evidence adduced by archaeology that primitive man was a sort of semi-beast did not indicate to him, as it did to others, that modern man was the product of slow mental and physical development. For Dawson, our barbarous predecessors were empirical evidence of the Fall. Mankind had been raised from this fallen state only by the Old Testament covenants and the Redemption of Christ. The Covenant with Noah, for example, was evident geologically in the marked amelioration of climate that followed the Ice Age. The physical effect of Christ's Redemption lay in the material and scientific progress that was granted to those societies which followed Christian precepts. Since Dawson believed that Christianity was responsible for contemporary progress, he argued that the domination of nature and improvement of human living conditions was not a result of evolution; in the economy of salvation, it was a useful by-product of the Good News of the Christian dispensation.

This view was another indication of Dawson's Paleyism and an extension of his earlier argument that the purity

49 *Ibid.,* pp. 75–76.
50 *Ibid.,* p. 185.

of Biblical science had been vitiated by accretions of Greek and medieval superstition. Dawson felt strongly on this point. He was quick to protest when John Tyndall, in his famous Address to the British Association for the Advancement of Science in Belfast in 1874, credited the atomistic philosophy of Democritus and Epicurus with a crucial role in the genesis of scientific thinking. Long before Democritus, he said, Moses had preached the unity of nature and soon afted Democritus the idolatries of ancient Greece overcame the atomistic philosophy.

> Historically, it is a fact that one Paul of Tarsus, a disciple of Moses and of Christ, had to preach to the Epicurians of Athens as late as the first century of our era, the doctrine of the unity of God, of nature, and of man.[51]

These lapses were incorporated into Dawson's thinking without any difficulty. His Calvinism led him to regard barbarism and idolatry as the normal state of unregenerate humanity. Dawson's attitude seemed to be: What else would one expect from fallen man?

About the Deluge which first mitigated human living conditions Dawson had almost nothing to say in *Archaia*. He added a short note to the effect that he accepted the interpretation of Pye Smith and Hitchcock who had maintained that the Deluge was explicable as a limited flood which *appeared* universal to the observer and was recorded as such. However, the cataclysmic aspect of the Biblical account of the Deluge raised some problems. Dawson accepted the opinion that the water for the Flood came from the Indian Ocean, yet geology had shown that changes in shore level generally proceeded slowly. He met this difficulty by positing a gradual subsidence that accelerated during the period of Noah's preaching. The Deluge which followed this subsidence occurred suddenly, probably because of a slight earthquake, a common enough phenome-

[51] J. W. Dawson, *Nature and the Bible* (New York, 1875), pp. 192–193.

non in Asia Minor, which altered the last few feet of water level and cascaded the ocean water over those who had not heeded Noah.[52]

Dawson repeated this account in his other books on the subject and presented a similar but expanded account again in 1895 in a small book entitled *The Historical Deluge.* A typical example of this expansion was his explanation of Noah's hesitancy about disembarking from the Ark. Noah, who knew unstable conditions when he saw them, hesitated because of the earth tremors that probably were a causal factor in the Flood and almost certainly continued when it was over.[53]

Dawson's interpretation of the Deluge was interesting because of its acceptance of the principle of untutored observation put forth by both Miller and Hitchcock. Dawson was not willing to accept their views on such issues as the sky as "firmament," the rain that fell out of the "windows" of heaven, or the earth that rested on "pillars." In these instances he either argued for a literal interpretation or he blamed the Greek translators for injecting their own superstitions. The source of this anomaly in Dawson's work was, apparently, tactical. If there was any possible way to preserve a literal reading, Dawson was determined to follow it; only if this were clearly impossible did he search for other means of accommodation. This point is important because it shows that when he had to choose between literalism and science, Dawson chose science. He took liberties with Hebrew that he would not take with geology.

Except for the adjustment of the catastrophic Deluge to uniformitarian geology, Dawson's exegetical work was largely confined to Creation, Eden, and the Fall. His only other contributions were in the form of brief notes: the re-

[52] Dawson, "Points of Contact," pp. 595–596.

[53] J. W. Dawson, *The Historical Deluge* (Chicago, 1895), pp. 18–19.

sults of the Ordnance Survey of Sinai nicely suited the account of the Exodus; the destruction of the Cities of the Plain was accomplished by a bitumen eruption, not unusual in the lower Jordan valley. In Dawson's view, Lot's wife not only got what she deserved, her fate was just what a geologist would suppose; she was encrusted in the saline mud which accompanies bitumen eruptions.[54] King Ahab received his just deserts scientifically, also. Dawson theorized that God used an ironic form of punishment for the idolatrous Israelites. Noting recent data showing a correlation between sunspots and drought, Dawson speculated that God afflicted Ahab through the very agency of his adopted sun god.[55]

Specific points such as Ahab and sunspots or saline mud and Lot's wife were typical of Dawson's reconciliation of Genesis and geology. His reconciliation rested primarily on a synthesis of specific Biblical passages with specific scientific ideas. However, he was also interested in the deeper philosophical issues underlying the tension between the new geology and the old interpretations of Scripture. The issue was the conflict between the catastrophism that existed throughout the Bible and the uniformitarianism of geology. Dawson's approach was to deny many of the alleged conflicts. He maintained, for example, that there was abundant evidence of immense (i.e., catastrophic) physical change at the close of each great geological era. Uniformitarian geology, he said, accepted occasional catastrophies as uniform parts of larger cycles.[56] Where this explanation was inapplicable, Dawson chose another tack: the issue was often semantic rather than geological. The face of a cliff, he declared, eroded slowly and uniformly

[54] J. W. Dawson, "Physical Causes of the Destruction of the Cities of the Plain," *The Expositor,* ser. 3, 3 (January, 1886): pp. 72–75.

[55] Dawson, "Points of Contact," pp. 580–581.

[56] Dawson, *The Origin of the World According to Revelation and Science,* p. 155.

over a long period of time, but when a huge chunk of rock fell from it the event appeared to be a sudden catastrophe. As in the case of the Deluge, Dawson fell back to the principle of the "untutored observer."

The issue was deeper than this, however. Dawson recognized that the tendency of uniformitarian thought was away from teleology. One of James Hutton's maxims was that geological processes showed "no vestige of a beginning, —no prospect of an end." This was unacceptable to Dawson, who referred to the "absurdity of believing in eternal succession." Dawson's response was to blend design and uniformitarianism by emphasizing the progressive, i.e., teleological, character of the paleontological record. The record showed "change and progress, and this in a *uniform* direction" [italics mine].[57]

Such meticulous concern over science and Scripture, on particular as well as broad issues, seems irrelevant today. Scientists and students of Scripture pay little attention to each other's work. Few, save extreme Fundamentalists, insist any longer on a close correlation between the Word and the Works of God. Indeed, it is tempting to dismiss the efforts of such exegetes as Dawson as irrelevant and Fundamentalist. To do so, however, would be a major misconception in the evaluation of nineteenth-century intellectual history; it would be to read it in terms of twentieth-century attitudes and accomplishments.

The use of this approach makes Darwin himself seem less than great. As Donald Fleming protested during the Darwin centennial, Darwin was "a greater man than many of the celebrators seem to think."[58] The same reductive technique has left Darwin's opponents beneath scrutiny.

According to this reading, Darwin and the Darwinians, though appallingly ordinary scientists, proceeded to vali-

[57] *Ibid.*, p. 78; Loren Eiseley, *Darwin's Century* (New York, 1958), p. 73.

[58] Donald Fleming, "The Centenary of *The Origin of Species*," *Jour. Hist. of Ideas* 20 (June–September, 1959): p. 446.

date their theories with an unbroken succession of favorable evidence. This was not so, however. The period between 1870 and 1900 was one of very mixed success for the Darwinians. The time available for evolution was reduced to an impossibly short period by Kelvin's physics. In 1900 scientists were still looking for an adequate mechanism for evolution. It was only Rutherford's physics and the new genetics that provided sufficient time and means for evolution to remain convincing.[59]

An analogous method of interpretation has been followed in intellectual history. Twentieth-century attitudes have been projected back into the nineteenth century. Since Fundamentalism has often been opposed to scientific developments in our time, it is commonly assumed that the same Fundamentalism dominated nineteenth-century opposition.[60] But such was not the case. There is a clear line of descent from the eighteenth century and William Paley to Pye Smith, Hitchcock, Miller, and Dawson. Dawson represented the long arm of Paley reaching out almost to the twentieth century.

This is not to say that the issue was fought out entirely between agnostic science, Paleyism, and Fundamentalism. Liberal, "Modernist" Protestants refused to accept such a narrow frame of reference and, after 1870, were increasingly successful in adjusting theology to science. Dawson's literalist approach to Scripture prevented him from making

59 The notion of a triumphant Darwinism is evident in a number of surveys of the thought of the period between 1870 and 1900. See Henry Steele Commager, *The American Mind* (New Haven, 1950), pp. 83–84; Merle Curti, *The Growth of American Thought* (3rd ed., New York, 1963), pp. 553–559; Richard Hofstadter, *Social Darwinism in American Thought 1860–1915* (Philadelphia, 1945), pp. 11–17.

60 See, for example, Bert James Loewenberg's articles "Darwinism Comes to America, 1859–1900," *Miss. Valley Hist. Rev.* 28 (December, 1941): pp. 346, 367–368, and "Evolution in New England, 1859–1873," *New England Quart.* 7 (June, 1935): pp. 234–243. Loewenberg sees the issue as one between empiricists and supernaturalists. This is a caricature of the conflict. The real conflict came between the new science and a third group, the latter day Paleyites, who insisted on integrating the natural and the supernatural.

the adjustments that other religiously inclined scientists were making. Asa Gray, for example, was able to synthesize his religious outlook and evolution. In fact, Gray, like Dawson, owed a great deal to Paley. However, while Dawson looked to nature for confirmation of the details of Scripture, Gray and other theistic evolutionists emphasized broader religious principles. Gray, in particular, attempted to find in the Darwinian notion of biological adaptation evidence of God's hand in nature. Modernism, now so clearly the middle ground, was a way out of his difficulties that Dawson refused to follow.

Dawson's great popularity as an author and lecturer was an index of the mass appeal of his position. He was in great demand as a lecturer. He gave the Phi Beta Kappa address in 1878 at Harvard on "The Rights and Duties of Science"; the chief rights and duties involved were to show the glory of God and the truth of Scripture.[61] He lectured at Princeton, Union, Columbia, and Crozer Theological Seminary. In 1886 Dawson was invited to lecture at the Brooklyn Institute on "the Power, Wisdom and Goodness of God as manifested in His Works." [62] Washington Gladden, the great Social Gospel leader and theological liberal, asked Dawson to contribute to *Sunday Afternoons* because he wanted "to have questions of science treated by religious men." [63] The great sale of Dawson's books was another indication that there was still a large audience for natural theology of the Paley variety.

For Dawson was no Fundamentalist in the present use of the term; neither was his work narrowly pietistic. As Professor Gillispie has noted in *Genesis and Geology,* pietistic religion is seldom concerned with natural theology.[64] On the other hand, liberal, ethically oriented Christianity

[61] Reprinted in *Princeton Rev.* 2 (July–December, 1878): pp. 673–679.
[62] C. L. Woodbridge to Dawson, November 6, 1886, Dawson papers.
[63] Washington Gladden to Dawson, November 5, 1877, Dawson papers.
[64] Gillispie, *Genesis and Geology,* pp. 7–8.

is likewise indifferent to welding the Word and the Works. Although Dawson was a literalist to the end, he and the Modernists addressed the same audience. This audience, neither fideistic nor rationalistic, lay somewhere between the extremes of Fundamentalism and naturalism. Dawson's many readers demanded that faith be made rational, that something like Paley's *Evidences of Christianity* be produced. It is in this light that Dawson's exegetical work is best understood.

# *IV. The Unity and Antiquity of Man*

NINETEENTH-CENTURY science did more than challenge conventional notions of cosmogony. The new anthropology and archaeology of the period between 1830 and 1860 struck hard at those who based their views on the traditional notion of the special creation of a single human species approximately six thousand years ago. The inheritors of the two theologies' tradition were hard pressed to maintain even the most general accuracy of the Bible. Revealed and natural theology became increasingly difficult to reconcile. No matter how liberally one looked at Scripture, it seemed that the universal parenthood of Adam and Eve could not be interpreted away. Yet anthropologists were offering convincing evidence that the several races of man were distinct species and, in the 1850's, all but the discredited Lamarckians knew that species were immutable. The only alternative seemed to be derivation of species or a separate creation and a separate parenthood for each race. The first challenged scientific orthodoxy; the second Scriptural orthodoxy.

Of the many scientists involved in this dilemma, none was more widely respected than Louis Agassiz. The chief proponent of the continental land glacier and protégé of the great Cuvier, Agassiz stood alone in pre-Civil War America as a scientist of international reputation. On his arrival in the United States in 1846, he was welcomed as a messiah. He traveled throughout the country on a lecture tour in 1847 and "every city . . . vied with its neighbors in the reception it gave him." [1] This popular reception was matched by a parallel prestige in the scientific commu-

[1] Edward A. Lurie, *Louis Agassiz: A Life in Science* (Chicago, 1960), p. 142.

nity. Agassiz was always a man to be reckoned with and never more so than in the 1840's and 1850's.

The imposing position of Agassiz made his conversion to the polygenist cause a grave matter indeed. One of his first stops in the United States was Philadelphia, where Samuel G. Morton, the leading American polygenist, held forth. While in Philadelphia, Agassiz examined Morton's collection of crania and saw Negroes for the first time. This "first contact with the black man was decisive"; Agassiz became convinced that the Negro belonged to a separate species.[2] His conviction was strengthened when, a few months later, he lectured in Charleston, South Carolina, and toured the local plantations.[3]

One of the results of Agassiz's decisive experience was a series of articles in the Unitarian *Christian Examiner* in 1850 and 1851. In these articles he upheld a potpourri of orthodox and heretical views: the notion of multiple creation of the same species in different geographical centers, the simultaneous creation of more than a single pair, the immutability of species, the specific diversity of man and the lack of Scriptural authority for the doctrine of the unity of man.[4] Agassiz's answer to the polygenist dilemma was to posit Biblical silence on multiple creations. He challenged his exegetical opponents to show any conclusive evidence of the doctrine of the unity of man in Scripture. On the other hand, he claimed indirect Biblical support for his view; after all, following his banishment, Cain married someone's daughter. Agassiz's articles came at a time when the other American polygenists—Morton, Ephraim Squier, and Josiah Nott—seemed to be producing a flawless case for

[2] William Stanton, *The Leopard's Spots* (Chicago, 1960), p. 103. Lurie, *Agassiz,* p. 143.

[3] Stanton, *The Leopard's Spots,* p. 154.

[4] Lurie, *Agassiz,* pp. 259–263.

the multiple origin of man. Squier, author of the influential *Ancient Monuments of the Mississippi Valley,* called Agassiz's work a "clincher." [5]

What the polygenists, Agassiz among them, had done was to present a dilemma to scientists who held to the unity *and* limited antiquity (4,000–6,000 years) of man. Those who held these positions were confronted with evidence from the mounds of the Mississippi Valley and newly opened Egyptian tombs that the American Indian and the Negro had not changed significantly in 4,000 years. Was it, then, reasonable to presume a change from white to black (Adam, somehow, was always a Caucasian) in as little as 1,000 years when no change had taken place since? The polygenist argument offered a difficult choice. One could still maintain the unity of man, if one was prepared to accept immense antiquity—a sufficient amount of time to account for the extremely slow rate of change shown by comparing skulls from Egyptian tombs with modern skulls. The other alternative was to jettison the unity of man and retain limited antiquity. Thus, one could maintain, compatibly with the new evidence, that the several races were created separately, not long before the Egyptian tombs were constructed.

Few voices were raised against this formulation of alternatives. Those who protested at all were clearly more interested in preserving unity at the expense of antiquity. John Bachman, an amateur naturalist and Lutheran minister in Charleston, South Carolina, protested vigorously in *The Doctrine of the Unity of the Human Race Examined on the Principles of Science* (1850). Asa Gray had begun his magnificent work on plant distribution mainly to show that migration from a single center was a more plausible explanation of distribution than multiple creation, and

[5] Stanton, *The Leopard's Spots,* p. 109.

Louis Agassiz was his target.[6] James Dwight Dana reviewed Josiah Nott and George Gliddon's *Types of Mankind* (1854) and made clear his rejection of the specific diversity of man.[7] Inasmuch as they tended to accept the notion of great antiquity for man, Gray and Dana, while denying polygenism, had approved the polygenist's dilemma.

The approach of Gray and Dana was not acceptable to William Dawson. Operating under the two theologies' principle, he saw no way of reconciling Scripture with *either* specific diversity or antiquity on the order of hundreds of thousands or even millions of years.

> In whatever way put, or under whatever disguise, it [polygenism] renders the Bible history worthless, reduces us to that isolation of race from race cultivated in ancient times by the various local idolatries, and destroys the brotherhood of man and the universality of that Christian atonement which proclaims that "as in Adam all die, so in Christ shall all be made alive." [8]

For his part, Dawson believed that innate superiority of the Caucasian race was not countenanced by either Scripture or science.

Dawson saw clearly the impact of polygenism on the entire species question; in his view the "rampant theorists of the new American ethnological school" were undermining the very foundations of science. The polygenist outlook applied not only to the unity of man; it brought with it chaos in defining any species.[9]

As the species question in general was the key to the problem for Dawson, so Louis Agassiz's particular treatment of the matter was the key to Dawson's attack on the

[6] Asa Gray, "Extract from . . . Memoir on the Botany of Japan in its Relations to that of North America . . . ," *Amer. Jour. Science*, 2nd ser., 28 (August, 1859): pp. 194–196. See also A. Hunter Dupree, *Asa Gray* (Cambridge, Mass., 1959), pp. 250–265.

[7] Stanton, *The Leopard's Spots*, pp. 169–170.

[8] J. W. Dawson, *Archaia* (Montreal, 1860), p. 246.

[9] *Ibid.*, pp. 247–248.

polygenist position. Agassiz had offered a new and disturbing definition of species in his *Contributions to the Natural History of the United States of America.* The definition was important enough to quote at length:

> Species is an ideal entity as much as the genus, the family, the order, the class, or the type; it continues to exist, while its representatives die, generation after generation. But these representatives do not simply represent what is specific in the individual, they exhibit and reproduce in the same manner, generation after generation, all that is generic in them, all that characterizes the family, the order, the class, the branch, with the same fulness, the same constancy, the same precision. Species then exist in nature in the same manner as any other group, they are quite as ideal in their mode of existence as genera, families, etc. . . .[10]

Dawson interpreted Agassiz's definition as an admission that species could not be defined without including along with the observed facts *a priori* notions on the question of specific unity. The definition was at best vague, at worst circular.

The circularity to which Dawson alluded was due to Agassiz's position in favor, not of mutability of species, but of multiple origin. Agassiz was "the only modern naturalist of eminence" who held this position.[11] In Dawson's opinion, there was convincing evidence that the conventional explanations of distribution sufficed in all but a few cases. Agassiz, on the other hand, offered little evidence for his heterodox views, but, rather, begged the question as far as distribution was concerned; he substituted "for evidence a definition of species altogether excluding the idea of common origin." Dawson charged that Agassiz had reversed the reasoning process; Agassiz first defined species (in the process excluding many of the usual criteria) and then

[10] Louis Agassiz, *Contributions to the Natural History of the United States of America* (Boston, 1857) **1**: p. 167.

[11] Dawson, *Archaia,* p. 282.

*deduced* conclusions as to the origin of species from the definition.

The main thrust of Agassiz's definition was to show that a species was an ideal rather than a real entity, a sort of category of understanding. For Agassiz, the only real phenomenon was the individual which, he was careful to say, only represented its species and did not constitute it. Dawson saw quickly what Agassiz was driving at. In order to maintain his position on multiple origin, Agassiz had forfeited the very basis of the species concept, i.e., that species was a reality and not simply a convenient concept. "For practical purposes, there may as well be no species at all." [12] Dawson saw the irony that many since have seen in Agassiz's denial of the reality of species and his simultaneous and vigorous defense of immutability. "On the principle that extremes meet," wrote Dawson, Agassiz's denial of real species "leads to precisely the same practical results with [*sic*] the Lamarckian hypothesis of transmutation." [13]

When he turned from Agassiz to develop his own approach to the question of the unity of man, Dawson followed his opponent's path and began with a definition of species. Species consisted of a "certain range of uniform characters." These characters were "invariably transmitted from generation to generation." In Dawson's opinion, the intervals between species "must be distinctly marked and not slurred over by intermediate gradations." The fact that specific distinctions could not be slurred did not mean that species did not vary; they did vary, said Dawson, but always within clear limits.[14]

[12] *Ibid.*, p. 290.

[13] *Ibid.*, p. 291. *Archaia* was written before *The Origin of Species* appeared. Dawson acknowledged in a footnote Darwin's original publication in the *Transactions* of the Linnean Society. He also passed a few negative comments on the basis of an abstract of Darwin's article which he had received. However, Dawson reserved extensive comment until he could study the full work; consequently, the evolution spoken of in *Archaia* is always Lamarckian.

[14] Dawson, *Archaia*, pp. 251–252.

This variation was the heart of the matter. How far could a variation proceed and still belong to the same species? Was it possible for a variation to exceed "specific limits"? More particularly, were the strikingly different characteristics of the North European and the Bushman beyond the limits of one species?

This last question Dawson answered with an emphatic no. He cited the traditional notion of the sterility of hybrids. Despite the allegations of Morton and Agassiz, he said, there was very scant evidence that hybrids were fertile. They were occasionally fertile with one of the original stock, but "if ever fertile *inter se,* which is somewhat doubtful, rapidly run out." [15]

The polygenists were confronted with a dilemma of their own on this issue. Faced with regular, not exceptional, fertility of mulattoes in the southern United States, they were forced to maintain that mulattoes were exceptions to the rule of sterility of hybrids or to admit that the races of man were not separate species, but varieties of one species. Some, like Agassiz, were prepared to make an exception to the rule. However, many polygenists were unwilling to grant either the dilemma or the fertility of hybrids. Josiah Nott, in an essay on hybridity in *Types of Mankind,* held that the mulattoes were in fact sterile but were kept in existence only because of wholesale promiscuity. Nott argued that continual and massive interbreeding with the white race explained the facts within the framework of the sterility of hybrids. Nott's argument infuriated Dawson; it was "monstrous and improbable" and most unflattering to Southern morality.[16] Dawson believed that it was only Nott's polygenism that had forced him to such improbable speculations. The more sensible explanation was that of the monogenist: mankind was one species and the varieties (i.e., races) were permanently in-

[15] *Ibid.,* p. 260.
[16] *Ibid.,* pp. 276–277.

terfertile. The commonly observed tendency of half-breeds to die out was, in Dawson's opinion, easily accountable on the basis of cultural and environmental factors.

In meeting the polygenist challenge Dawson had to deal with more than a definition of species and a charge of mass promiscuity. The diversity of his opponents' arguments matched the diversity they claimed for man. For example, a celebrated argument of another polygenist, Peter A. Browne, was based on alleged differences in the hair of the various races. The white man, as usual, provided the criterion. In this case, he had "perfect hair," while the Negro had hair like wool, hair that could be felted. In the first blush of American ethnology such distinctions weighed heavily in some quarters.[17] Dawson maintained that the variations between Negro and white hair did "not exceed the differences in the hair from different parts of the body of the same individual." Dawson noted further that the evidence adduced by Browne pointed "to no greater variety than that which occurs in many domesticated animals" and, thus, was no evidence of specific diversity.[18]

The most important evidence raised by Dawson against the polygenist case was that of known cases of extensive change *within* recognized specific limits. Dawson noted that many polygenists assumed that the production of a significant variety required a great length of time. The defenders of orthodoxy received unexpected assistance from Charles Darwin. While on the *Beagle,* Darwin had stopped in Argentina, where he learned of the case of the Niata cattle, a markedly different variety of cattle that had originated suddenly only a century earlier. He had also found evidence of extensive variation in a very short time in the rats of St. Helena and the Galapagos.[19]

[17] Stanton, *The Leopard's Spots,* pp. 150–154.
[18] Dawson, *Archaia,* p. 267.
[19] *Ibid.,* p. 256.

In this regard, Dawson himself noted that, in a few short centuries, the horses of Sable Island, off the coast of Nova Scotia, had degenerated to the level of Highland ponies.[20] There was also evidence of equally rapid change in humans. Dawson cited a much discussed case of sudden appearance of facial hair in a Burmese family; this case was especially significant, he said, because the characteristic had thus far proved to be permanent.[21] The evidence of such rapid change was crucial, since it answered the dilemma put forth by the polygenists; the separate races could still be varieties of one species and they still could be only 6,000 years old.

In addition to these negative arguments, Dawson presented a positive case for monogenism. His case was based on three factors: climatic influence, geographical distribution, and new developments in philology.

The philological argument was especially attractive to Dawson because it was in this field that new developments favored monogenism. The celebrated work of Max Müller had shown that the "tree of language" followed a course remarkably close to probable patterns of human migration. Dawson was even more impressed by linguistic analogies. He thought that language was analogous to species; like species, language was distributed over wide areas and was influenced by environment. Most important, language varied greatly while retaining its "specific" character. Dawson argued that modern philology had shown that varieties of the great Indo-European language were spoken from the Ganges to the west coast of Ireland.

> No one now doubts the affinity of this great belt of languages. No one can pretend that any one of these nations learned its language from another. They are all decided branches of a common stock.[22]

"All the more eminent philologists," he said, held to the

[20] *Ibid.*, p. 258.
[21] *Ibid.*, p. 279.
[22] *Ibid.*, p. 294.

unity of language and their testimony provided powerful opposition to polygenism, opposition that could not be ignored.[23]

The strength of the philological argument rested to a great extent on the correlation between language and probable paths of migration. Dawson held that patterns of distribution afforded positive evidence for the unity of species. He found Agassiz's proposal of multiple origin of species to be wildly speculative. "We cannot be required to assume a cause greater than the effect demands"; where one center of creation was sufficient, the probabilities favored the single origin of species.

Agassiz had chosen as examples of the multiple origin of species widgeons and ducks that were, by common judgment, distinct on each side of the Atlantic.[24] He inferred that, since these species had been separately created on each side of the Atlantic, the Mallard and Scaup ducks, common to both sides, had also been separately created. In Dawson's opinion, Agassiz's choice of the Mallard and Scaup ducks was as unfortunate as his method of reasoning. The Mallard, Dawson said, had demonstrated extraordinary capacity to adapt; in its case, migration was much more probable than multiple creation. The Scaup duck, on the other hand, was extremely hardy. Since it was carnivorous and, more important, very seaworthy, its capacity for migration was even greater than that of the Mallard.[25]

The polygenists were closing their eyes, said Dawson, to the abundant evidence of *observed* distribution over wide areas. Two common species of rats had spread over most of the world within recorded history. The horse, ox, and hog had demonstrated that they needed only transportation across oceans to distribute themselves over most of the globe. From a geological point of view, the evidence of former land connections between continents made the cur-

23 *Ibid.,* p. 299.
24 Agassiz, *Contributions* **1**: p. 40.
25 Dawson, *Archaia,* pp. 287–288.

rent need of artificial transportation seem insignificant. Man himself provided the most striking instance of extensive distribution. The northern European seemed able to thrive in most regions; the Malay race had defied climate and ocean to spread over a huge area of the Pacific. In Dawson's opinion, the attempt to establish diversity on the ground of distribution, though "sanctioned by so great a name as that of Agassiz," failed "most signally of all in the case of man." [26]

The attempt to establish diversity represented only part of the problem put forth by the polygenists; the other side of the dilemma concerned the antiquity of man. Since Dawson was unwilling to grant either great antiquity or diversity, his work in this area brought him, for the first time, into direct conflict with his friend and mentor, Sir Charles Lyell. When Lyell published *The Geological Evidences of the Antiquity of Man* in 1863, Dawson was distressed to find a persistent implication of the great antiquity of man. Lyell, one of the most discreet of men, had produced several hundred pages of evidence that led towards a conclusion of great antiquity. To make matters worse, Lyell's book culminated in a series of chapters that were very favorable to Darwin and Huxley.

Lyell presented a difficult target, for he studiously avoided taking unequivocal positions. His writing was a strange mixture of crystal clear exposition and ambiguous or equivocal evaluation. For example, Lyell avoided transposing geological evidence for great antiquity into specific lengths of time; he wrote of post-Pliocene man without dating the Pliocene.[27] When dealing with controversial topics such as evolution and the antiquity of man, it was his

[26] *Ibid.*, pp. 291–293.

[27] The term post-Pliocene was used generally through most of Dawson's career. Sir Charles Lyell, the great arbiter of geological terms for English speaking geologists, did not drop the term until 1873. Dawson used it almost exclusively until 1883, when with most other geologists he substituted "Pleistocene." The simplest and least confusing course was to use both terms as they naturally arose in the material discussed. Thus, throughout this work "post-Pliocene" and "Pleistocene" have the same meaning.

custom to imply rather than state his conclusion. The nearest he came to a clear statement of his position in *The Geological Evidences of the Antiquity of Man* was the remark that

if the advent of man in Europe occurred before the close of the second continental period, and antecedently to the separation of Ireland from England and of England from the continent, the event would be sufficiently remote to cause the historical period to appear quite insignificant in duration, when compared to the antiquity of the human race.[28]

However indirect such statements might have been, Lyell's connotation was clear enough. He implied that Western European man had been a contemporary of such extinct species as the mammoth and that the mammoth had become extinct in Western Europe a very, very long time ago. A second important and challenging implication of Lyell's was that man had existed in Western Europe before great changes of elevation which must have required a vast lapse of time.

It was these implications that most concerned Dawson when he wrote a lengthy review of Lyell for *The Edinburgh New Philosophical Journal* in January of 1864. Dawson saw quickly that the correlations of man with extinct species and great changes of level were harmless in themselves; the overriding question was the time involved in these correlations. The tack that he followed, then, was to heap praise on Lyell's book, while denying the need for great antiquity. Thus, Lyell's work was "very valuable" and, as a result of its excellence, others were now able to form their own judgments on the great questions at hand. Lyell himself was eulogized as "one of our greatest masters of inductive reasoning." [29]

[28] Sir Charles Lyell, *The Geological Evidences of the Antiquity of Man* (London, 1863), p. 289.

[29] J. W. Dawson, "On the Antiquity of Man," *New Edinburgh Philos. Jour.*, N.S., 19 (1864): pp. 40–41.

Dawson was his master's pupil; he was no more forthright than Lyell. Dawson's veiled implications were that Lyell, while a great popularizer and anthologizer, did not always draw the proper conclusions. He lauded his preceptor's inductive powers and ignored completely Lyell's deductive abilities. Dawson praised Lyell for his presentation of an encyclopedic array of facts and used the same facts to establish very different conclusions. For example, among the facts adduced by Lyell were the discoveries of the Engis and Neanderthal skulls, with their prominent superciliary ridges, and the presence of human remains in the Danish peat bogs at levels that suggested great age.

As far as the Danish peat was concerned, Dawson pointed out that the calculations of age were based on the growth rate of peat and the succession of the different trees that had formed the peat. Such calculations were, he said, "obviously unreliable." [30] The order of succession of species was from pine to birch or poplar, then, to oak, and finally, to beech. This was familiar ground for Dawson; one of his first published papers, which had appeared sixteen years earlier in the same journal, dealt with precisely this question in North American forests.[31] According to Dawson, the forest of pine was very vulnerable to fire; "it might perish in this way in a single summer." The second growth of poplar or birch would then form a new forest within half a century and "in two or three centuries would probably be succeeded" by a forest of oak.[32] The oak forest could survive for centuries or, if conditions were right, be replaced by beech in a relatively short period. Dawson's conclusion was that "all the changes observed in Denmark" could have occurred within 2,000 years.[33]

[30] *Ibid.*, p. 42.

[31] J. W. Dawson, "On the Destruction and Partial Reproduction of the Forests in British North America," *Edinburgh New Philos. Jour.* 42 (1847): pp. 259–271.

[32] Dawson, "On the Antiquity of Man," p. 42.

[33] *Ibid.*, p. 43.

Dawson found the evidence of the human skulls no more convincing than that of the peat bogs. He cited the opinion of T. H. Huxley that the skull supposed to be the oldest, that found in a cave near Engis in Belgium, was "not by any means abnormal." The Neanderthal skull, said Dawson, was still much controverted; however, the major characteristics of this skull were still found "in the rude tribes of America and Australia." [34] Dawson thought it doubtful that the Neanderthal remains represented a separate variety of man; it was more probable, he said, that they belonged to men who had run wild and lived on the outskirts of more civilized communities.

Here, again, Dawson was his master's pupil. His technique was to apply the canons of Lyell's own uniformitarianism to show that the facts to be explained required no great length of time. According to the uniformitarian method of interpreting the past in terms of existing causes, the Danish peat bogs were formed by changes in forest cover that were still at work in the great wooded areas of the world such as eastern Canada. In these areas, the changes often occurred rather rapidly. Likewise, the cave skulls, on which so many arguments for both the antiquity and derivation of man depended, could all be matched with *existing* skull types. The crania that Dawson had in mind were those of North American Indians. He believed firmly that Lyell and other European scientists would drastically revise their estimates of man's antiquity once they became sufficiently well acquainted with the North American analogies.

The estimates of Lyell and his European counterparts were based, in many cases, on the association of human bones with those of extinct animals. Here, too, Dawson was skeptical. Such associations were not "free from the suspicion" that they were merely accidental mixtures; "this

[34] *Ibid.*, pp. 53–54.

suspicion still applies to some of the cases cited by Sir C. Lyell, as more or less certain proofs." [35] Dawson was willing to grant, however, that the evidence for the correlation of human remains with several extinct species—*Elephas primigenius, Rhinoceros tichorinus,* and *Ursus spelaeus*—was overwhelming. His reaction to this correlation was to pose a question: "When did the fossil mammals named above really become extinct?" [36]

The answer to this rhetorical question was, of course, that these species had not been long extinct. The only acceptable method of converting the period implied by this correlation into solar years, said Dawson, was to calculate "how long a time would be occupied by agencies now in operation." On this principle, it was commonly assumed that a great amount of time was necessary. It was Dawson's contention that the uniformitarian position in this regard was often very narrowly stated. He held that modern rates of change, the rates on which the projection of antiquity was based, were untypically slow in a number of cases. The famous calculations based on the rate of erosion in the channels of the Somme, the St. Lawrence, and the Mississippi were all predicated on erosion during non-glacial conditions. In the light of new evidence showing that the glacial period was more recent than had been supposed, "the whole calculation of time must be revised." Dawson argued that the effects of frost, ice-jams, spring freshets, and a greater volume of water would have increased the rate of erosion far beyond current estimates.[37]

Although a uniformitarian himself, Dawson was very dubious of the application of uniformitarian principles by many of his contemporaries. He protested the nearly exclusive use of the rates of change of western Europe and what he regarded as uncritical acceptance of the modern

[35] *Ibid.,* p. 57.
[36] *Ibid.,* p. 59.
[37] *Ibid.,* pp. 59–61.

period as typical. This modified uniformitarianism served Dawson well. It allowed him to have his cake and eat it; when he wanted to shorten man's antiquity, he could debunk the acceptance of modern conditions and rates of change; when he wanted to attack the notion of derivation of species, he could himself take an uncompromising uniformitarian position and argue that, since no species had been derived in the modern period, none had *ever* derived from another.

Although it must have been a bit irritating for Lyell to have his own guns turned against him by one of his own protégés, equanimity was one of his many virtues and he made no direct response to Dawson's negative review. However, a few years later, in 1868, Dawson published a second edition of *Acadian Geology,* dedicated, as was the first edition, to Lyell. The new edition contained much of the material from Dawson's review of 1864. When Lyell wrote to express his appreciation of the dedication, he took the opportunity to rebut a number of Dawson's suggestions. The work on the Danish peat bogs was much more reliable than Dawson had claimed, said Lyell. In response to Dawson's supposition that a series of forest fires hastened the succession of trees, Lyell noted that such a rotation "brought about by general conflagrations is too catastrophic to suit my notions, and would require some monuments of the work of fire," yet the peat showed no evidence of fire.[38] The tone of this brief exchange was cordial, however, and the relations between the two men continued to be very close.

After the lengthy review of Lyell, Dawson was silent on the question of man for nearly ten years. He had his hands full keeping the wolf away from the gates at McGill. During this period his major scientific concerns were considerably lower links in the chain of being, notably *Eozoön cana-*

[38] Lyell to Dawson, July 1, 1868, in Katherine M. Lyell (ed.), *Life, Letters and Journals of Sir Charles Lyell, Bart.* (London, 1881) 2: p. 425.

*dense* and primitive Devonian plants. It was during this period that his most significant work in these two areas was done, the Devonian articles in 1859 and the early 1860's, the *Eozoön* polemics between 1865 and the early 1870's.

When Dawson again turned his attention to man in 1874, he had much more than polygenism to grapple with. By 1874 Darwinism was a widespread and firmly rooted outlook. From Dawson's point of view, polygenism paled to insignificance in the face of this new threat. There was a bright side to the threat for the monogenist, however. Dawson found it possible to lay aside the question of derivation and to interpret *The Origin of Species* as showing the great capacity of species to vary; Darwin, for all his heterodoxy, dealt a mighty blow to polygenism.

Dawson appropriated *The Origin of Species* for his own purposes by the simple device of accepting its conclusions as they related to variations, while denying that these conclusions showed derivation. Thus, when Darwin produced persuasive evidence of evolution, Dawson interpreted the results as showing, not derivation, but the pronounced tendency of many species to vary widely—as the monogenists had maintained all along. Dawson termed the resulting phenomenon a new variety, not a new species. Where Darwin's results indicated a variation beyond recognizable specific limits, Dawson argued that he was simply wrong. He took full advantage of the difficulties that Darwin experienced in precisely determining specific limits. When it suited his purpose, he accepted Darwin's evidence, but not his definition of species. In other cases, Dawson recognized Darwin's definition, but challenged the evidence of derivation. Such nimble semantics enabled Dawson to use *The Origin of Species,* while avoiding the pitfall of evolution:

> Many so-called species are probably races or varieties and one benefit of these inquiries [e.g. Darwin's] has been to direct attention to the proper discrimination of species from varieties among ani-

mals and plants. The loose discrimination of species, and the tendency to multiply names, have done much to promote evolutionist views.[39]

Monogenism became a more tenable position after Darwin. The effect of *The Origin of Species* and of the works of Gray and Hooker on plant distribution was to place the polygenists on the defensive. Agassiz's hypothesis of multiple origin became less persuasive and the truly racist element in the polygenist ranks soon discredited itself. The traditional doctrine of the unity of man seemed more secure than ever by 1874.

However, Darwin, Gray, Hooker and their colleagues secured unity only at the expense of antiquity. Instead of polygenism, they posited a single human species which was widely distributed and, therefore, had varied greatly. However, wide distribution of species was a very slow process; in fact, it was a general rule that the wider the distribution the longer the time needed. This left man, one of the most widely distributed species, with a past much longer than conventional readings of the Bible allowed.

It was not surprising, therefore, that when Dawson again wrote on man, in 1874, his chief interest was in limiting man's antiquity. There were several ways in which he did this. He pointed to the absence of human remains in older strata; since there was no clear evidence of man in the Pliocene, he said, man was postglacial.[40] Even a limitation to the postglacial period was too extensive, unless this period itself were shortened. Dawson set about to shorten the post-Pliocene geological record by noting that, although the record was clear, the time involved was not. The record in western Europe, the area in question, showed plainly a period of subsidence followed by a period of re-elevation. The key to the time problem was the speed of these move-

[39] J. W. Dawson, *The Story of the Earth and Man* (New York, 1874), p. 328.
[40] *Ibid.*, p. 283.

ments. Here Dawson had to confront again his own and Lyell's uniformitarianism; by a strict uniformitarian reading, these changes in level would have taken an unacceptably long period of time. Dawson's resolution of this conflict was to fit an occasional catastrophe into a larger uniformitarian framework—a catastrophe without catastrophism. Thus, Europe could take what Dawson termed a "plunge bath" without necessitating a return to catastrophism.[41]

Dawson's speculation was that between the Pliocene and the Pleistocene the rotation of the earth slowed and that this retardation caused water to be driven towards the poles, submerging western Europe. The weight of this water eventually became too great and the earth at the equator collapsed; the tectonics of this collapse then caused western Europe to be rapidly re-elevated.[42] Dawson confidently asserted that the pendulum of scientific opinion would swing back on the question of rates of change, as it had done on polygenism.[43]

The rapid subsidence and re-elevation posited by Dawson was not particularly important in itself. Its significance lay in its relation to the various cave deposits of western Europe. Had the debris which covered alleged human remains accumulated slowly over millennia or had it poured into the caves quickly in one of the paroxysms of Dawson's speculation? One of the first steps at this level of argument was to show that the calculations of great age "have all been shown to be more or less at fault; and possibly none of these reach further back than . . . six or seven thousand years." [44] Pursuing this tack, Dawson reinterpreted several significant cave deposits, notably Kent's Hole in Devonshire. It was this cave, he said, that had

[41] *Ibid.*, pp. 290–291.
[42] *Ibid.*, pp. 291–292.
[43] *Ibid.*, p. 293.
[44] *Ibid.*, pp. 292–293.

done most to impress British scientists with the notion of the great antiquity of man.

Dawson argued that the only measurements of time that had been applied to Kent's Hole were the rate of stalagmite growth and rate of erosion in neighboring valleys. These measurements, he held, were unreliable. As far as Dawson was concerned the only reliable index of time was the sequence of events. In this regard, it was probable that the cavern was first cut by the sea and that the first inhabitants were cave bears much like existing Arctic bears. These bears, whose bones were found in the lowest cave deposits, lived on fish. As the land rose, the cavern was elevated "perhaps several hundreds of feet" above the sea. The deposits in the cave during this period were due to mountain torrents which carried stones, mud, and the carcasses of a wide variety of animals. Along with the carcasses came human weapons. The absence of human remains themselves, Dawson said, was an indication of the high state of the men of that time. These men were too strong and intelligent to die often from accidental causes and too civilized to bury at random; they were not found in caves such as Kent's Hole because they probably had special places of sepulture. The next major change shown by the cave deposits was a second subsidence. The deposits of this period contained evidence of human habitation, probably a tribe taking refuge from the encroaching winter. The last step in the cave's history involved a re-emergence from the sea and another, last, period of human habitation, this time by relatively recent ancestors.[45]

This account was, in Dawson's opinion, not controversial. The point in question was the time involved. Dawson maintained that the measurements which indicated a great length of time were "obviously worthless" and that the changes of level—the key to understanding the deposits

[45] *Ibid.*, pp. 307–309.

—could have occurred very rapidly. Dawson made clear that his idea of rapid change, i.e., "plunge bath," was a matter of a few thousand years.[46]

The length of time indicated by the cave deposits, however, was only one factor to be considered. Another, more important, aspect of the problem was the nature of the human remains themselves. In the opinion of most scientists, a vast gap in time was implied in the striking differences in anatomy between fossil and living Europeans. Differences of skull conformation were particularly significant. Dawson regarded the anatomical distinctions as dubious. In his opinion, none of the fossil human skulls differed greatly from the typical modern skull; the range of difference was no greater than that between existing human skulls. As an example Dawson cited again the Engis skull, which he compared to recent skulls of Algonquin Indians. Dawson found the cranial characters of these specimens very similar: "Anyone acquainted with cranial characters would readily admit that the ancient Belgian may very well have been an American Indian." [47]

The critical reaction to such notions was less than cordial. Asa Gray, for example, did not let friendship with Dawson interfere with a scathing review of *The Story of the Earth and Man.* "This is droll reading," was Gray's acid comment.[48] An anonymous reviewer in *Nature* was more direct: "We think it hardly necessary to make further comment on the work in question, except to hope that it will not fall into the hands of . . . students." [49]

In *The Story of the Earth and Man,* Dawson failed to develop his suggestion that a parallel could be drawn between the men of the caves and the Indians of Canada. His

[46] *Ibid.,* p. 309.

[47] *Ibid.,* p. 357.

[48] Asa Gray, *Darwiniana,* ed. A. Hunter Dupree (Cambridge, Mass., 1963), p. 204.

[49] *Nature* 9 (January 8, 1874): p. 180.

sole concern had been to debunk the anatomical evidence of great antiquity. However, always an opportunist, Dawson soon saw more positive uses of these cave discoveries. In an article in 1879 in *The Princeton Review,* he noted that, according to the Bible, shortly before the Flood there arose "a mixed race of men, strong physically, with fierce passions, daring, adventurous, and cruel, who lorded it over the earth and deprived others of their natural rights and liberties." [50] Fossil hominids such as the Engis specimen were, in Dawson's opinion, remains of these men. The versatile skull from Engis, then, resembled both the Algonquin Indians and the giants that were in those days!

Dawson chose to develop still more fully the notion that the cave deposits contained remains of uncivilized portions of early human society. This line of development offered another opportunity to strike at the immense antiquity that many scientists inferred from the great difference between modern man and the cave deposits. Though he was prepared to accept many of these differences, Dawson had argued since 1864 that it was misleading to compare the cave remains with modern Europeans. Dawson had at various times proposed the "plunge bath" in place of slow change, cranial similarities as opposed to cranial differences, and the human remains in the caves as a "savage remnant" rather than typical men of the time. By 1880, he had gathered his sporadic observations into a unified hypothesis in *Fossil Men and Their Modern Representatives.*

The theory, dubbed by Loren Eiseley the "wild man" hypothesis, synthesized Dawson's ideas on the controverted gaps in time, culture, and anatomy.[51] Early man, in Dawson's view, had been highly civilized, as civilized as existing

[50] J. W. Dawson, "Points of Contact between Science and Revelation," *Princeton Rev.* 4 (November, 1879): p. 592.

[51] Loren Eiseley, *Darwin's Century* (Garden City, N. Y., 1958), p. 274.

North American Indians. He argued that clay beads found in deposits in Sweden showed that it was entirely possible that paleolithic men could make pottery. Even if they could not make such artifacts, their inability

> would prove not so much their barbarism as their nomadic mode of life, and they may have made and used, like the North American hunter tribe, the most beautiful baskets and bark boxes which would serve their purposes better than rude pottery.[52]

Dawson was in the untenable position of citing missing artifacts as evidence of the existence of a missing culture. Although he recognized the general weakness of his case, he contended that the evidence was lacking only because it lay beneath the sea. Arguing by analogy with traditional patterns of settlement, Dawson maintained that it was only reasonable to suppose that his hypothetical civilized settlements had been submerged in the general Pleistocene subsidence of western Europe. The same analogical mode of thought led Dawson to postulate the existence of barbaric tribes that had broken off from the main stock and had become depauperated—as, he said, the wild Veddahs of Ceylon were degraded Aryans and the Hottentots and Bushmen were "depauperated descendants of that great Ethiopian nation which in Upper Egypt founded one of the oldest known civilized kingdoms." [53]

Since their civilized contemporaries rested conveniently beneath the waves, these "wild men" were all that remained for modern archaeologists to find. The error of these archaeologists had been to accept remains such as the Engis skull as representing the highest state of human development in paleolithic time. This error, combined with uniformitarian notions of an extremely slow rate of change, was at the base of the claim for great antiquity. In Daw-

[52] J. W. Dawson, *Fossil Men and Their Modern Representatives* (London, 1880), pp. 97–98.

[53] *Ibid.*, pp. 68–69.

son's view, the truth of the matter was that, on the one hand, the change of level occurred suddenly, while, on the other, the men of the caves were untypical specimens—as untypical as the North American Indians were of the gas-lighted and steam-driven culture of the nineteenth century! To illustrate this last point he presented photographs of two living Chippewa chiefs—surely two of the most fearsome who ever drew a bow—as evidence that reasonable facsimiles of paleolithic man were still living and that they existed as satellites of civilized centers such as Detroit, Toronto, and Montreal.[54] The analogy, said Dawson, pointed to one conclusion: the cave deposits could easily be remains of a wild, satellite society and this society need not be very old.

The errors of European archaeologists on the question of man's antiquity were, in Dawson's opinion, a result of the "desultory and imperfect references" to American archaeology and anthropology. Such casual treatment of American science was a persistent irritant to Dawson (as it was to most scientists in the United States). It was Dawson, for example, who proposed the term "Erian" as a more appropriate designation for the European "Devonian."[55] In the *Eozoön* controversy, Dawson was continually annoyed by the refusal of his opponents to look at the alleged fossil *in situ*. The price paid for neglect of this sort was error, he said, and never were the errors more significant than on the antiquity of man. The unquestionably recent savage past in North America was an indication that the savage past of Europe was likewise more recent than was commonly believed. A decent respect for North American archaeology would have corrected "some of the fanciful and enthusiastic impressions" that were current.[56]

[54] *Ibid.*, p. 252.

[55] "Erian" is still used in North America as a major subdivision of the Devonian.

[56] *Ibid.*, pp. 3–4.

A case in point, argued Dawson, was the similarity of the skeleton and sepulture of a Cro-Magnon warrior found in a cave at Mentone to that of the North American Indians who fought with Champlain. The similarity extended to the shell-plaited cap, headdress with teeth, arrows, bracelets, anklets, and traces of iron oxide that probably indicated war paint.

> Could this old brave of Mentone, belonging to a tribe whose very name is unknown to history, spring again into life, he would, in garb, arms, and appearance, have shown no marked difference from the tribes that inhabited the St. Lawrence valley three hundred years ago.[57]

In Dawson's view, this was not a far-fetched case. The parallel between the savages of Europe and America extended to the use of wampum. New work on geographical distribution showed the likelihood of migration from one continent to the other; this, in turn, made a genetic relation a distinct possibility.

Dawson wrote *Fossil Men and Their Modern Representatives* in Montreal, a city that was built on the site of the old Indian village of Hochelaga. The McGill campus, in fact, rested on Indian remains and the excavations for the many buildings constructed under Dawson's aegis regularly produced artifacts for his study. For those who thought his analogies far-fetched, Dawson suggested an examination of the Hochelaga remains.

Jacques Cartier had visited Hochelaga and left a description that was accurate enough to locate the village three hundred years later. Cartier's account included a description of a well-developed society with a highly sophisticated division of labor. It was Dawson's contention that in three short centuries the remains of Hochelaga had come

[57] *Ibid.*, p. 142.

to resemble those of the European caves that he had visited:

> The remains, when disinterred, are veritable fossils; everything perishable, even hair and the animal matter of bones, has disappeared. Nothing remains but stone and pottery and charcoal, and the mineral matter of bones, which underground might remain unchanged for a hundred centuries as well as for one. Nothing but Cartier's visit of a few hours duration prevents us from being in a position to attach to these remains the longer date with as much show of reason as the shorter.[58]

Dawson's argument, like so many nineteenth-century scientific arguments, rested primarily on analogy. He was attempting to replace one set of analogies with another. The opposition had presented a chain of analogies that involved immense temporal and cultural gaps between fossil man and modern man. Dawson's response was a fruitless attempt to substitute another group of analogies that drastically reduced these same gaps.

Dawson wondered, rhetorically, why it was that his opponents began their analogies with the assumption that contemporary savages were the primeval type of man. The usual procedure of paleoanthropologists, said Dawson, had been

> to gather up and parade all that is discreditable and low in the condition and manners of the modern savage, so as to approximate him as nearly as possible to brutes; and having done this, to exhibit him as the existing representative of our prehistoric ancestors.[59]

The end result of this process was a misleading view of the origin as well as the antiquity of man. Hochelaga, Dawson argued, showed that it was possible for a very sophisticated society to leave remains that were almost undistinguishable from many of the European cave deposits.

Dawson was very proud of *Fossil Men and Their Modern Representatives;* he wrote in his autobiography that

[58] *Ibid.*, p. 102.
[59] *Ibid.*, pp. 68–69.

"this book is, in my judgment, one of the best I have written."[60] A less enthusiastic but still favorable judgment was given by the anonymous reviewer of Edward Drinker Cope's *American Naturalist,* who, while unwilling to accept Dawson's conclusions, admitted that "it is but fair to say that his [Dawson's] profound knowledge of paleontology has enabled him to present the brachychronic view of archaeology more forcibly than . . . any other recent writer who has made the attempt."[61]

Another anonymous reviewer, writing in *Nature,* took a different tack. He said that enthusiasts were always stepping forward to show that the sun goes around the earth after all or to find "no difficulty whatever in squaring the circle."

> It seems uncertain whether Prof. Dawson, of McGill College, Montreal, is to be classed with these malcontents, or whether his scientific heresies are to be explained as conforming to the general law that superstitions generally survive and even thrive in colonies long after they have died out in their mother country.[62]

This reviewer found Dawson's detailed and imaginative discussion of Hochelaga to be more formidable than the rest of the book. However, he had little difficulty in pummeling the *non sequitur* involved in Dawson's use of the *possibility* of errors regarding Hochelaga as evidence of the *actual existence* of errors in the evalution of European archaeological discoveries. He objected to the religious tone in Dawson's book and, especially, to hints that modern scientists should repent of more than scientific error; when it came to repentance, he said, one could only repent of having read Dawson's book.[63]

[60] J. W. Dawson, *Fifty Years of Work in Canada* (London and Edinburgh, 1901), p. 130.

[61] *The Amer. Naturalist* **15** (February, 1881): pp. 154–155.

[62] *Nature* **22** (May 27, 1880): p. 82.

[63] *Ibid.*

Perhaps deterred by such a scorching review, Dawson wrote very little on the question of the unity and the antiquity of man during the 1880's. This was the period of his most energetic political activity in scientific societies, however, and his work in other areas showed a similar pause. When he began writing again, Dawson was in poor health and semi-retirement. Nevertheless, he published several books after 1890 and in one of them, *The Meeting Place of Geology and History* (1894), he returned for the last time to the old battleground.

Dawson began his final consideration of man's antiquity with a survey of some of the developments that had taken place since 1880. Chief among these was Kelvin's work in physics which sharply circumscribed the age of the earth. Dawson pointed out that according to the latest estimates the earth could be no more than twenty million years old; the widest latitude that could possibly be claimed for man's existence was 250,000 years. In Dawson's opinion, the age of the earliest unquestionably human remains was less than 10,000 years.[64]

A second area of significant development between 1880 and 1894 was the discovery of many new human remains. Dawson surveyed some of this new evidence and found it wanting. He noted that no one claimed to have found traces of man in the earliest epoch of the Tertiary, the Eocene. This period was worth mention only because of its importance to evolutionists; if later humans had evolved, there must have been intermediate forms in the Eocene.[65] The links were still missing, however, and Dawson expected them to remain so.

[64] J. W. Dawson, *The Meeting Place of Geology and History* (London, 1894), p. 21. This was, of course, before Ernest Rutherford showed that the age of the earth was billions of years.

[65] Dawson, like Lyell, was unwilling to translate terms such as Eocene, Miocene, Pliocene, and Pleistocene into solar years; hence, it is difficult to determine exactly the time periods he had in mind.

Similarly, there was no direct evidence of man in the Miocene. The only evidence was indirect—"worked flints" that had been found in several French localities and were in Dawson's view, of dubious value. Their artificial or "worked" quality was questionable; their location in the Miocene was controverted. Dawson suggested that it was also possible that the flints had been fashioned by apes working through instinct, much as beavers building dams—very intricately, but not intelligently.[66]

Moving to a more recent period, Dawson raised similar objections to the authenticity of Pliocene remains in America. He cited the work of W. H. Holmes of the United States Geological Survey as evidence of the doubt "on geological grounds" that had been cast on the existence of preglacial man. Holmes had investigated excavations made for a sewer in Trenton, New Jersey, and had discovered that worked flints found on the site were not part of a layer of Pliocene gravel but were made from debris lying against this gravel. Modern Indians, not Pliocene men, had used the debris to make flint weapons.[67]

Dawson was also skeptical of alleged human remains in the Pliocene of Europe. He argued that a skull found in the Pliocene deposits in the Val d'Arno, which he was compelled to admit was "of modern type," "may have been brought down from the surface by a landslip." Dawson added that the human characteristics of some of the other known Pliocene deposits were most doubted by the very scientists who were most interested in extending man's antiquity. For example, a cave at Castelnodo, near Brescia, contained a skull that was more advanced than any known Pleistocene skulls. Since this showed retrogression, said Dawson, it was the orthodox evolutionists—usually most

[66] Dawson, *Meeting Place,* p. 28.
[67] *Ibid.,* pp. 32–34.

interested in authenticating Pliocene remains—who were leading the skeptics.[68]

One of the main reasons for the perplexity over deposits such as the Castelnodo skull was that Dawson and his nineteenth-century colleagues were, like the rest of their culture, very much Europe-centered. Many of them found it difficult to think of early man, except in relation to Europe and Asia Minor. Dawson shared most of these pre-conceptions and he found it particularly hard to accept the premise that man, in Europe and Asia Minor, could have survived the cold of the glacial age and other great physical changes of the early Pleistocene and modern periods. The notion of an African or an Austral-Asian genesis was either not considered or was dismissed, as Dawson himself dismissed Haeckel's "Lemuria," calling it a pipedream.

In his last book on the subject, as in his first, Dawson presented a consistent, coherent analysis of the problem of man's antiquity. He maintained that early man had experienced a series of catastrophes; what he chose to call the Palanthropic Age (in place of Paleolithic) came to a very definite and "tragic end." [69] This end, he said, was too often overlooked by writers who had a prejudice in favor of slow, almost imperceptible change, a prejudice dictated not by uniformitarian geology, but by Darwinism.

Dawson's point was that many scientists had gratuitously applied geological principles to anthropology.[70] This was a very misleading technique, in his opinion. A change which, from a geological point of view, was very slight and gradual, was catastrophic from a human or anthropological perspective. A tidal wave was a uniform event for geology

[68] *Ibid.*, pp. 28–29.

[69] Dawson almost invariably chose his terms in the light of larger considerations. In this case he was concerned that Paleolithic implied an undue savagery and separation from modern man, so he substituted a term that implied simply a fossil form of modern man.

[70] *Ibid.*, p. 85.

but a catastrophic one for inhabitants of coastal plains and the period in question had experienced much greater dislocations than tidal waves. Dawson protested strongly that these dislocations were being overlooked; he termed "desperate" the attempts to discredit the abrupt nature of the change from one period to the other.[71]

The point that Dawson was making was an important one. Although his particular outlook was antiquated even in 1894, his insight was keen. What he was saying was that uniformitarianism was a two-edged sword, that could just as easily be used against evolution and the new archaeology. In this respect, at least, Dawson was ahead of his time, for the ambivalence of uniformitarianism has only recently been pointed out.[72]

The ambivalence was due to the fact that uniformitarianism projected existing causes and conditions into the past. The key, then, to the use of this outlook was the precise nature of present conditions. Dawson recognized this and set out to establish a group of facts that pointed towards his conclusions and which could, on the uniformitarian principle, be extended into the past. To do this he advanced the notion of a limited catastrophism.[73] Along with limited catastrophism, he stressed aspects of present conditions that showed the proximity of modern man to fossil man. It was important for Dawson that the gap between different human forms be narrowed, while the gap between ape and man be widened. This explains Dawson's occasional celebration of the high state of Cro-Magnon and Neanderthal man; it also explains his work on North American Indians. Just as limited catastrophism could sharply reduce the time available for man's existence, and

[71] *Ibid.*, p. 91.

[72] See, for example: Walter F. Cannon, "The Uniformitarian-Catastrophic Debate," *Isis* 51, 1 (March, 1960): pp. 38–39, 54–55; William Coleman. "Lyell and the 'Reality' of Species: 1830–1833," *Isis* 53, 3 (September, 1962): p. 331.

[73] Dawson preferred a more positive phrase—"modified uniformitarianism."

a higher cultural state could indicate that Neanderthal man was not, after all, such a remote ancestor, so the Indians could show that a great gap in culture did not require a great gap in time.

Dawson used the Micmacs and Chippewas where his opponents used deposits in caves, mounds, and the Egyptian tombs. He did this because the dilemma first posed by the new ethnologists and anthropologists in the 1830's was still very much alive. Dawson's opponents used the evidence accumulated in the intervening sixty years to widen the cultural gap between fossil man and modern man and to narrow the paleontological gap between man and other species. Dawson, a scientific counter-revolutionary, vainly attempted to reverse the process, to widen the paleontological gap and narrow the cultural gap. His strategy was sound; it was betrayed only by facts.

# *V. The Species Problem*

THE SPECIES problem has been of perennial interest to scientists. The received opinion prior to the nineteenth century was that the earth had been populated with a fixed number of species by the "sixth day" of creation and that these species had then reproduced with only limited variations. This immutability had been questioned by men such as Benoit de Maillet, Pierre de Maupertuis, and the Comte de Buffon who thought it more likely that God had created a few broad types from which conventional species had derived. For the most part, however, scientists in 1800 were convinced that species were immutable. Another French naturalist, Jean Baptiste de Lamarck, introduced the subject to scientific controversy in the early years of the century and discussion simmered continuously until *Vestiges of the Natural History of Creation* was published in 1844. The ensuing outrage over what was deemed scientific humbug and an attack on Providence in nature was a preview of what was to come in 1859 with the publication of *The Origin of Species.*

Dawson had followed the attacks on *Vestiges of the Natural History of Creation* very closely and was a fervent admirer of Hugh Miller and *The Footprints of the Creator,* the latter's contribution to the assault. Dawson had even offered a small contribution to the discussion as early as 1847, when he wrote for *The American Journal of Science* "On the Destruction and Partial Reproduction of Forests in British North America." The purpose of his article was to show the extent to which plants could adapt to changes in environment as a means of showing the great variability of forest life *within* specific limits. He thought that such an inquiry would help dispel

> the mystery which frequently envelopes the succession of organized beings in circumstances of physical change; a mystery which has induced some naturalists to recur to the doctrine of spontaneous generation and the transmission of species.[1]

Dawson's own position was clear: species were specially created by God and were immutable. How long ago God created the earth did not concern Dawson. He accepted the consensus of the day which placed the age of the earth at about one hundred million years. As far as time was concerned, Dawson's only interest was to maintain the position that man had not been created more than six thousand years ago. On this point he was intractable. Dawson also believed that all species, including man, could vary widely and rapidly within certain distinct limits. This was a position that Dawson maintained consistently and defended vigorously for the next fifty-two years. In 1847 he held this view in common with most of his scientific colleagues; at the time of his death in 1899 he was one of the dwindling handful of competent scientists who still held that species were immutable.

The interest in the species question that had simmered for decades and had flared up after the publication of *Vestiges of the Natural History of Creation* became the preoccupying concern of the entire intellectual world after the appearance of Darwin's *The Origin of Species.* At this time Dawson was actively engaged in a related area, the polygenist controversy, and was following ancillary developments very closely. He was, for example, one of the few men who noted the original publication of Darwin's

[1] J. W. Dawson, "On the Destruction and Partial Reproduction of Forests in British North America," *Amer. Jour. Science,* 2nd ser., 4 (November, 1847): p. 161. This article was also published in *Edinburgh New Philos. Jour.* in the same year.

and Wallace's papers in the *Journal* of the Linnean Society in 1858.

Already alerted, Dawson read *The Origin of Species* with dismay. It seemed to him that Darwin had used his great talents and immense accumulation of valuable material to buttress a hopelessly old-fashioned theory. Dawson was lavish with praise for Darwin's book as a much needed study of the nature and extent of variation. However, he could not understand Darwin's extension of variability beyond specific limits; neither could he accept Darwin's constant allusions to struggle in nature. For Dawson, nature was like Archdeacon Paley's watch and he saw the hand of the Clockmaker everywhere. His evaluation of Darwin's book, therefore, was mixed:

> These pearls are not the less valuable to the judicious reader, that the author has seen fit to string them upon a thread of loose and faulty argument, and to employ them to deck the faded form of the transmutation theory of Lamarck.[2]

For Dawson, Darwin's misadventures were typical of those of many scientists who were not content to remain silent in the face of the unknowable. "True science is always humble, for it knows itself to be surrounded by mysteries." It was natural, said Dawson, for a distinguished naturalist such as Darwin to want to solve mysteries; such was the destiny of students of nature. However, some scientists were "content cautiously to explore the ground and prudently to retreat where to advance is no longer safe"; others, less discreet, gathered "all their strength for a rush and a leap into an unknown and fathomless abyss." [3] Despite his many achievements, Darwin was, in Dawson's opinion, an instructive example of the indiscreet scientist.

[2] J. W. Dawson, "Review of 'Darwin on the Origin of Species by Means of Natural Selection,'" *Canadian Naturalist and Geologist* 5 (February, 1860): p. 118.

[3] *Ibid.*, p. 100.

Dawson began his detailed analysis of *The Origin of Species* by noting that the book should be considered from two points of view: first, as a careful and very impressive study of the laws of variation, and second, as a "wild and fanciful" application of these laws beyond specific limits.[4] From the first point of view, Darwin's book received high marks from Dawson. Darwin, he said, had demonstrated the great variability of species more clearly than anyone else, "in opposition to many views maintained with much vigour on this side of the Atlantic." This last comment was a general allusion to the "American School" of anthropology. Dawson aimed a more particular reference at his old antagonist, Louis Agassiz; Darwin imposed "a salutary caution on those naturalists who too readily admit geographical distribution as an evidence of specific distinctness."[5]

Despite these positive comments, Dawson's reaction to *The Origin of Species* was (and remained) extremely unfavorable. Like many paleontologists, his response was dominated by the thought that "we have species which have remained distinct in the whole period of human experience, and also as far back in geological time as we can trace any of them."[6] Dawson objected to what he considered Darwin's subtle shifting of the burden of proof. Throughout *The Origin of Species* Darwin treated species in a thoroughly agnostic manner; for him the stability or mutability of species was a completely open question. Darwin began his investigation with the attitude that there was no evidence one way or the other on the derivation of species. This enabled him to treat very lightly the received opinions on species. Darwin's attitude irritated Dawson, who protested that there was considerable evidence in favor of

[4] *Ibid.*, p. 101.
[5] *Ibid.*, p. 118.
[6] *Ibid.*, p. 103.

the stability of species. The burden of proof, he insisted, rested with Darwin.

The question of burden of proof involved more than a debater's trick. Dawson pointed out that Darwin's agnostic attitude had a substantive bearing on several key points. The most notable of these points was the tendency of varieties to revert to original types. Such a tendency, Darwin admitted, would overthrow completely that portion of his argument based on variation under domestication.[7] Darwin protested that a common phenomenon in nature was the appearance of a variety produced "by external causes applied in domestication," which would promptly lose its "acquired . . . characteristics" and revert to its original state when these causes were removed.[8] For Dawson and for most scientists in 1859, this phenomenon was evidence of an original type. Darwin, however, posited not an original type, but, rather, new causes of change which encouraged adaptation in another direction. The fact that this direction resembled a previous state of the organism was for Darwin merely accidental.

Darwin's position assumed that species were destitute of distinctive characteristics to begin with. Since the prior existence of specific characteristics was one of the questions in dispute, Dawson rightly charged Darwin with employing a circular mode of argument and with ignoring the evidence for stability of species. Darwin, he claimed, was able to argue that the disappearance of acquired characteristics was adaptation rather than reversion only because he assumed the truth of what was to be proved.[9]

Dawson was especially concerned with Darwin's use of the evidence obtained from domestic pigeons. These findings, applied strictly to variation within specific limits, Daw-

[7] Charles Darwin, *On the Origin of Species, a facsimile of the first edition* (Cambridge, Mass., 1964), pp. 14–15.

[8] Dawson, "Darwin on the Origin of Species," p. 102.

[9] *Ibid.*, pp. 102–103.

son welcomed as the most valuable portion of *The Origin of Species.* It was the further application, to speciation, that bothered Dawson. Just as some critics were to say, in effect, of the famous *Drosophila* experiments, "after all they are still fruit flies," so Dawson said of Darwin's pigeons, "the pigeon, with all its varieties, is still a pigeon." [10] Properly interpreted, Darwin's evidence was, in Dawson's opinion, powerful support for the immutability of species.

Dawson admitted that the differences produced in pigeons by variation under domestication were great. However, variation and speciation were very different matters. He maintained that the differences involved mainly nonessential characteristics, such as color and development of feathers. No change on a specific level had occurred, said Dawson, and it was a gross misconception of the evidence to conclude, as Darwin had, that some of the variations could extend beyond species to the generic level.[11] Furthermore, many of the variations cited by Darwin were abnormal to the point of monstrosity; these could not be classified properly as specific differences. The varied pigeons were perfectly interfertile, while the overwhelming evidence still favored the traditional notion of the sterility of hybrids. Finally, Dawson argued that Darwin's own account showed that cross-breeds tended to revert to the characteristics of the rock-pigeon, "showing that the specific type remains uneradicated." [12]

Dawson's objection to Darwin's agnostic attitude towards species was strong, but his rejection of natural selection was even more forceful. Dawson could not accept the idea that "nature" selected; from his point of view, the laws of nature gave only "a certain tendency to vary, the

[10] *Ibid.*, p. 112; Gertrude Himmelfarb, *Darwin and the Darwinian Revolution* (London, 1959), p. 366.

[11] Darwin, *The Origin of Species,* pp. 316–317.

[12] Dawson, "Darwin on the Origin of Species," p. 109.

extent of which is the point in question." [13] Noting again the tendency of varieties to revert, Dawson argued that Darwin was asking his readers to believe

> that those same natural courses which break down all the breeder's elaborate distinctions so soon as his breeds are allowed to intermix and live in a natural way, are themselves able to take up the work and do still greater marvels in the way of selection.[14]

Dawson also rejected the struggle for existence as the mechanism for accomplishing selection. For him, the struggle was "a fancied warfare in nature, in which the race is always to the swift and the battle to the strong." Dawson could not understand Darwin's equation of the breeder's care and pampering with the course of toil and starvation involved in the struggle to survive. Improvement through breeding he could understand, but struggle, he thought, "should deteriorate and degrade species, as we know it has done in every case of the kind that we have observed." [15] Species that were under severe environmental pressure, such as the red deer of Scotland, degenerated rather than improved. The struggle for existence, in Dawson's opinion, was a myth "and its employment as a means of improvement still more mythical." [16]

Dawson also attacked the Malthusian basis of Darwin's hypothesis of struggle as a means of originating species. The English clergyman and economist, Thomas Malthus, had contended in his *Essay on Population,* written in 1798, that animals reproduced at a geometrical rate, while food supply increased arithmetically. The result, said Malthus, was that sooner or later population outstripped food supply and weaker individuals starved. The Darwinian notion of the "preservation of favoured races" was greatly in-

[13] *Ibid.,* p. 110.
[14] *Ibid.,* p. 112.
[15] *Ibid.*
[16] *Ibid.,* p. 113.

fluenced by Malthus. The Malthusian doctrine, "though good for a single species viewed by itself, is false for the whole in the aggregate." According to Dawson, vegetable life and low forms of animal life, the nutritional support for most of nature, increased at a much faster rate than the forms which subsisted on them. The truth of the matter was that vast quantities of food went to waste. It was typical of Dawson to see God's design where Darwin saw struggle: the excess of food seemed to be the reason for the "hordes of scavengers . . . that seem *specially created* [italics mine] to gather up the fragments of nature's bounteous feast." In nature, said Dawson, "there is always enough and to spare." [17]

It was in the field of paleontology that Dawson was most qualified to comment on *The Origin of Species* and it was here that he found Darwin's work most wanting. The lengthy discussion in *The Origin of Species* of the imperfection of the fossil record, he argued, did "not mitigate the condemnation of the selection theory pronounced by geology." Dawson was more concerned with the perfection of the fossil record in many significant areas. There were many deposits "where the profusion of specimens and continuity of formation preclude any supposition of much imperfection in the evidence." Dawson was familiar with two such areas, the Silurian limestones of America and "the plant-bearing beds of the coal formation." In both of these areas the evidence revealed some species which persevered through many consecutive deposits, while others suddenly appeared and disappeared; in no case did the record in these areas show specific change.[18]

Dawson's conclusion was that "in those parts of the geological scale which are the most perfect and unbroken, there

[17] *Ibid.*, pp. 112–113.
[18] *Ibid.*, p. 116.
[19] *Ibid.*

is no graduated transition of forms."[19] His own work on post-Pliocene shell deposits in the Gulf of St. Lawrence indicated that out of more than sixty species, not one had varied more than its living relatives. Several of these, although no longer living in the Gulf of St. Lawrence, survived *unchanged* in the Arctic seas. They had been forced into the Arctic by warmer water; "they had plenty of time to vary, in order to suit the new circumstances, but they could not." Facts such as these were conclusive, "notwithstanding the imperfection of the geological record on other points."[20]

If one accepts all of Dawson's criticisms of *The Origin of Species,* the deficiencies of the fossil record seem minor, compared to those of the book itself. The task of the reviewer, said Dawson, was hopeless, "for it would require a book as large as the original to expose the fallacies which appear in every paragraph."[21] Nevertheless, science was much in Darwin's debt; the failure of such an accomplished investigator would give pause to others. A trifle over-optimistic, Dawson concluded that Darwin's failure would "give an eternal quietus to the Lamarckian hypothesis."[22]

Attacks such as those of Dawson did not quiet the clamor that arose around the "Lamarckian hypothesis." The continuing controversy led Dawson to apply to the species question research originally begun for wholly different purposes. Sir Charles Lyell and Dawson, in 1842 and again in 1851, had jointly investigated a group of amphibians and reptiles preserved in the coal deposits near Joggins, Nova Scotia. These animals, *Baphetes, Dendrepeton, Hylonomus,* and *Hylerpeton,* were the highest forms of life known in the Carboniferous. These rocks also contained the remains of a land snail, *Pupa vetusta,* and a mil-

[20] *Ibid.,* pp. 116–117.
[21] *Ibid.,* p. 115.
[22] *Ibid.,* p. 120.

lipede, *Xylobius sigillariae.* The combination of great age and high development was full of anti-evolutionary potential. It is not surprising, therefore, that, faced with Darwin's challenge, Dawson exploited the possibilities presented by these remains.

In 1863 Dawson published an eighty-one-page monograph, entitled *Air Breathers of the Coal Period,* which was a thorough exposition of the whole discovery. The monograph was composed almost entirely of material that Dawson had published in the *Quarterly Journal of the Geological Society of London* between 1853 and 1856. However, he added nearly ten pages at the end of *Air Breathers of the Coal Period* which made explicit the relevance of the early reptiles and amphibians to evolution.[23]

While he was unwilling to affirm definitely that the "air breathers" were the oldest creatures of their type, Dawson thought that the probability of their being so was overwhelming. Proceeding on this supposition, he questioned whether these organisms could be presumed to have derived from other forms.

> It would be easy to build up an imaginary series of stages, on the principle of natural selection, whereby these results might be effected; but the hypothesis would be destitute of any support from fact, and would be beset by more difficulties than it removes.[24]

No evolutionist, said Dawson, dared to claim that a snail or millipede could have evolved into an amphibian or a reptile. The only reasonable prospect for the origin of the latter two lay in the fishes of the Devonian period.

Here the links were better established. Dawson admitted that "all known coal reptiles have leanings to fishes in certain characteristics." Yet the gap still yawned wide, he hastened to add; a comparison of a reptile such as *Hylono-*

[23] J. W. Dawson, *Air Breathers of the Coal Period* (Montreal, 1863), pp, 73–81.

[24] *Ibid.,* p. 77.

*mus* with Devonian fishes showed, not improvement or development, but rather the introduction of entirely new organs. The foot of *Hylonomus,* he asserted, "bears perhaps as close a relation to the fin of a fish as the screw of one steamship to the paddle wheel of another, or as the latter to a carriage wheel." [25] The difference between the Joggins fossils and any possible predecessors were so great that the latter "must have existed from a time earlier than any in which even fishes are known to exist." [26] This meant that the derivationist himself must have recourse to "sudden and as yet unaccountable transmutation"—a position that did not differ greatly from the traditional concept of special creation. For the facts as known in the case of the "air breathers," special creation was as reasonable as any evolutionary explanation.

The primitive amphibians and reptiles of the Carboniferous represented to the inveterately theistic Dawson links in the chain of being, evidence of the "will and plan of the Supreme Mind":

> They are the handiwork of our Father and our God, traces of his presence in primeval ages of the earth, evidences of the unity of his plan and pledges of its progressive nature.[27]

In his long review of *The Origin of Species* as well as in *Air Breathers of the Coal Period,* Dawson had difficulty in distinguishing Darwin's ideas from those of Lamarck. By 1869, when he next wrote on evolution, he suffered from no such confusion. In fact, the subject of his presidential address to the Natural History Society of Montreal in that year was precisely the differences between the evolutionary hypotheses of Lamarck, Darwin, Richard Owen, and Edward Drinker Cope.

25 *Ibid.,* p. 78.
26 *Ibid.,* p. 79.
27 *Ibid.,* p. 80.

Dawson noted at the outset that Lamarck took a much more philosophical approach to nature than did Darwin. As Dawson phrased it, "Lamarck supposed animals to be acted on by an attractive influence from before, Darwin by a propelling influence from behind." [28] Darwin and Lamarck still had much in common, however; Lamarck laid great stress on the influence of the environment and of habits acquired by organisms as a result of external circumstances, "in which respect his theory differed less than is generally supposed from that of Mr. Darwin." [29]

Dawson regarded Owen's speculations on evolution as even more philosophical than Lamarck's. Owen's concept of an innate tendency to deviate from parental type was, for Dawson, little more than a "mere statement of belief in derivation." The chief scientific aspect of Owen's thought that interested Dawson was the notion that evolution was completely independent of external circumstances. In this regard Owen was occupying a position which was clearly different from that of other evolutionists; it was not a position Dawson found attractive. He thought Owen's arguments were "feeble" and that the latter's position on evolution could be reduced to a circular proposition: "species change because they tend to change." [30]

Evolution as proposed by Darwin was clearly not circular. Darwin, whose work had been under close scrutiny for nearly a decade and was gaining adherents every day, offered a much more formidable obstacle than Owen. Dawson's approach to Darwin in 1869 was, correspondingly, more circumspect than it had been in 1860. Nevertheless, he thought that Darwin's difficulties were many and that three "fatal" objections could be raised to natural selection as "a sole mode of accounting for derivation." The first of

[28] J. W. Dawson, "Modern Ideas of Derivation," *Canadian Naturalist and Quart. Jour. of Science* 4 (July, 1869): p. 132.

[29] *Ibid.*

[30] *Ibid.*, pp. 123, 132.

these fatal objections had been an important element in Dawson's review of 1860: the observed fact that struggle seemed to result in deterioration rather than improvement. A second objection was the fact that no specific derivation had ever been observed. Thirdly, Dawson asserted that, from a geological point of view, the amount of time required by Darwin was impossibly long.[31]

On the issue of time Dawson was quite insistent; he went to those great bones of contention, the alleged horse sequence. The great American paleontologist, Othniel C. Marsh, had accumulated a fossil series that showed steady progress from a small, doglike creature, *Paleotherium,* to the modern horse. For the sake of discussion, Dawson granted that *Paleotherium, Hipparion,* and *Equus* were indeed links extending from the present back to the early Cenozoic. The question immediately arose, he said, whether this sequence offered a basis for tracing a line of descent further back from *Paleotherium* to an ultimate predecessor. According to Dawson no such extension was possible. If one applied to earlier periods the rate of change shown by the alleged derivation of *Equus* from *Paleotherium,* the time required would stretch back far beyond any known placental mammals. The only remaining possibilities for evolutionists were the discovery of new fossils or derivation from either primitive marsupial mammals of the late Mesozoic or from reptiles.

The first of these possibilities offered as much to the opponents of evolution as it did to supporters of the hypothesis. New fossils might well have upset the sequence. Of the latter two possibilities, said Dawson, the first, derivation from primitive marsupials, was most unlikely because of the magnitude of the change from marsupial to placental and the narrowness of the gap in time between the appearance of the two forms. For the second of these possibili-

[31] *Ibid.,* pp. 132–133.

ties, even evolutionists were agreed that, if Mesozoic reptiles had changed into anything, it was into birds, not mammals.[32]

The objection on grounds of time limitations was directed at natural selection as a means of evolution, rather than at derivation itself. Dawson was convinced that natural selection could account for only the slightest and the slowest of changes. It is not surprising, therefore, that he cast a more friendly eye at the neo-Lamarckian views of Edward Drinker Cope. Cope's hypothesis was based on the alleged analogy between embryonic changes and the historical development of genera. To this analogy Cope added the Lamarckian notion of the inheritance of acquired characteristics. He synthesized these ideas through the Lamarckian concept of "vital force." Each living thing possessed this force, he claimed, and could direct it towards particular organs and away from others; the controlling factor in directing "vital force" was use and disuse. The effect of this channeling of "vital force" was to stimulate or retard development of particular characteristics. Since acquired characteristics were inheritable in Cope's view, such changes were passed on to subsequent generations. Cope's Law of Acceleration and Retardation, which was put forth independently and almost simultaneously by Alpheus Hyatt, went one step further: a change in one generation occurred either earlier or later in subsequent generations, depending on use or disuse.

Cope, in Dawson's opinion, overcame many of the difficulties encountered by Darwin. Cope and the neo-Lamarckians had the credible mechanism for evolution that the Darwinians were lacking. Acceleration provided for relatively rapid change and, hence, met the time problem very well. Finally, and perhaps most importantly, the effect of evolution as proposed by Cope on the edifice of

[32] *Ibid.*, p. 126.

natural theology was minimal. Design was still present in nature; God still cared enough to give His creatures a constructive capacity to adjust; better yet, law still ruled in His domain.

The ready adaptability of Cope's views to traditional theology was very attractive to Dawson. On strictly scientific grounds, Dawson found Cope's theories the "most promising" of all the evolutionary hypotheses. Instead of vague speculations, Cope offered a wide variety of observed facts. Where facts were not available, Cope's theories were capable of being tested eventually, said Dawson, while Lamarck, Owen, and Darwin (Dawson lumped them together on this point) offered unverifiable theories. On the basis of Cope's achievements, Dawson was optimistic about the prospects for embryology providing important clues to a "law of creation"—a term he preferred to either derivation or evolution.[33]

One of the most spectacular facts that drew Dawson towards Cope's views was a startling phenomenon that had recently been noted in the United States. The great Yale paleontologist, Othniel C. Marsh, had observed the axolotl, a species of *Siredon,* change into an entirely different form. The change was all the more remarkable because it transcended specific limits and seemed to represent a change beyond even the generic level, from fish to reptile. The fact that the change required a warmer temperature than the axolotl was accustomed to seemed to confirm neo-Lamarckian views of the influence of environment in stimulating adaptation.

Dawson was one of the many swept up in enthusiasm for the apparent breakthrough represented by the axolotl. Unfortunately for Cope and his followers, the "fish" was soon found to be merely a larval stage of *Siredon,* a true reptile. The startling phenomenon was due to the fact

[33] *Ibid.,* pp. 136–137.

that the cold water in the lakes of the Rockies from which the axolotl was taken prevented maturation of the organism.

Dawson ostensibly received Cope's work warmly; however, he still clearly preferred no evolution at all to any development theory, including Cope's. He welcomed Cope's investigations only in so far as they contributed to the establishment of a "law of creation." The semantics of this term are somewhat difficult. By it, Dawson did not mean theistic evolution as that phrase is customarily used; neither did he mean orthogenetic evolution. Dawson's "law of creation" was, more accurately, a rather flexible form of special creation, that could include a significant amount of development without derivation of one species from another.

Despite these hazy semantics, it is fair to say that by 1869 Dawson's attitude towards evolution had changed. He was careful to distinguish Darwin from Lamarck. He was much more willing to grant some role for development. If Cope's variety of evolution was not entirely palatable, neither was it unacceptable. Finally, by 1869 it was clear that the renewed attention to the species question was not a momentary fad. Dawson had treated Darwin in a rather casual manner in portions of his review in 1860. By 1869 Dawson was taking a more sober, scientific approach to the whole question; he recognized belatedly that Darwin was here to stay.

Dawson's address was well received by at least two notable American scientists, James Dwight Dana and Alpheus Hyatt. Dana wrote to Dawson to thank him for a copy: "Your arguments with regard to Darwin and Owen are excellent." His only complaint was that Dawson had been too accommodating to Cope, particularly on the question of *Siredon*. In Dana's judgment, *Siredon* had "nothing of the permanence of a species" and was therefore irrelevant to the whole issue of derivation.[34]

Alpheus Hyatt wrote to Dawson to express satisfaction that he

> had given expression at last to the feelings with which we had viewed the exceeding haste of the European world to swallow Darwinism without winking.
>
> Under the shelter of your first protest, for such it really is . . . , we may hope to hear from others of humbler rank on this side of the water.

Hyatt, too, complained about Dawson's treatment of Cope; however, his remarks differed sharply from those of Dana. Hyatt claimed precedence in formulating the Law of Acceleration which Dawson had attributed to Cope.[35]

In the 1860's Dawson began a pattern of response to evolution that continued for almost forty years. On the one hand, he registered a vigorous rebuttal to major statements of evolutionist theory, while, on the other hand, he used the results of his own work to buttress the anti-evolutionist position. Whether by chance or design, it happened that several of his major endeavors had a ready application to evolution; three of his fields of specialization involved the first appearance of particular organisms: *Eozoön canadense,* the "air breathers," and Devonian plants.

Dawson's work on Devonian plants was especially promising for creationist purposes. The preceding flora, that of the Silurian, had been very limited. The succeeding formation, according to Dawson, the Lower Carboniferous, was likewise very poor in plants. Dawson was able to argue that the Devonian flora had no credible antecedents, became extinct for no known reason, and left few credible successors. A further explanation for Dawson's use of the

[34] Dana to Dawson, August 7, 1869, Dawson papers.

[35] Hyatt to Dawson, March 31, 1870, Dawson papers. Hyatt's appeal was successful; after 1870 Dawson customarily credited the Law of Acceleration to both Hyatt and Cope.

Devonian flora was that he was the world's leading authority in this area of paleontology and felt certain that he had the answers.

In an important article on evolution and Devonian plants in the *American Journal of Science* in December of 1871, Dawson set out to show that a large number of clearly defined species were "not rationally deducible, on any theory of derivation, from those known in other periods." [36] He listed some fifty-one "certainly distinct specific types" of plants in the Devonian of Nova Scotia. It was impossible, he said, to account for these forms on the basis of derivation from Upper Silurian plants since only two or three of the species existed at that time. On the other hand, only four of the Devonian species reappeared identically in the Carboniferous. Dawson granted that no less than twenty-six species were found in the Carboniferous in allied forms "which a derivationist might claim as modified descendants." [37] The more important fact, he said, was that the remaining twenty-one forms were totally unknown in the Carboniferous. The absence of these species, combined with the presence in the Carboniferous of a large number of plants not accountable on the basis of anything known in the Devonian, was, in Dawson's judgment, a very serious challenge to all theories of evolution.

The challenge was all the more serious because in at least one case the Devonian flora showed an extremely advanced and specialized development. *Syringoxylon mirabile,* named by Dawson almost certainly with this argument in mind, showed, he asserted, that the evolutionists' insistence that highly developed organisms could only be produced by derivation from more primitive predecessors should be regarded skeptically.

[36] J. W. Dawson, "On the Bearing of Devonian Botany on Questions as to the Origin and Extinction of Species," *Amer. Jour. Science,* 3rd ser., 2 (1871): p. 411.

[37] *Ibid.,* pp. 414–415.

Dawson was also convinced that the evidence of the Devonian plants made natural selection a much less plausible mechanism for evolution. Natural selection, he asserted, simply could not explain rationally the extinction of some plants and the preservation of others. "Where single types disappear, under circumstances in which others of similar habit continue," natural selection failed to account for the observed phenomena. Dawson argued that in such circumstances it was more reasonable to assume that "such types may have been in their own nature limited in duration, and may have died out without any external cause." [38]

Dawson's article in 1871 on evolution and Devonian botany was the first in a rapid series of attacks that went far beyond his earlier articles in both extent and vehemence. By 1871 few scientists were as actively engaged in the anti-evolutionist cause. Of those few, Dawson was one of an even smaller number who kept up a sustained attack.[39] As Alpheus Hyatt's letter in 1870 implied, Dawson was acquiring a public reputation as an opponent of Darwinism. He was not long in living up to this nascent reputation.

Dawson returned to the attack in his presidential address to the Natural History Society of Montreal in May of 1872. On this occasion his remarks bore for the first time a stamp of hysteria that had not marked his earlier articles. For the first time, Dawson's vision of the social and religious horror attendant on Darwinism was openly stated. Darwinism, he said, had a tendency to prostitute natural history to the service of a shallow philosophy. Left unchecked, the new outlook would lead to "the destruction of science, and a return to semi-barbarism." [40] One can-

[38] *Ibid.*, p. 412.

[39] Philip G. Fothergill, *Historical Aspects of Organic Evolution* (London, 1952), p. 122n. Fothergill notes that most critics of Darwin registered their objections in single papers.

[40] Quoted in *Nature* 45 (June 20, 1872): p. 150.

not help thinking that, had social Darwinism never existed, men like Dawson would have conjured it into being.

Dawson continued his assault in 1873, addressing each new sally to a larger audience. In August he spoke before the American Association for the Advancement of Science, at Portland, Maine, and in October to a more general and much larger assembly in New York, the General Conference of the Evangelical Alliance, where he had a featured place on the program. His last and most extensive anti-evolutionary effort in 1873 was a widely read popular treatment of the question in *The Story of the Earth and Man.* As the size of his audience grew, Dawson's vehemence increased commensurately.

At the meeting of the A.A.A.S. Dawson rose in floor discussion to challenge the evolutionists present to show that there had been successive progress from lower to higher organic forms. What proof, he asked, could be brought forward for this proposition? The record of the rocks showed that degradation was just as common as improvement. According to Dawson, "the most ancient form of man is beyond the average standard of modern humanity." He must have had two of his friendly adversaries from Harvard (Louis Agassiz and Asa Gray) in mind when he gibed: "If the man of Cromagno[n] or Mentone had been sent to Harvard, he would have been graduated with full honours." [41]

Dawson outwardly welcomed the research of the evolutionists. Their work had improved standards of classification and had served to expose many artificial "species." Sanctimoniously and, in retrospect, ironically, Dawson expressed concern for the reputations of the derivationists, because "they have chosen a mistaken path." While unfortunately destroying their own reputations, these scientists were, nevertheless, slowly establishing a correct theory. In Dawson's view, the theory that would outlast the

[41] Quoted in *Nature* 8 (September 11, 1873): p. 392.

current controversy was special creation of species with a "plastic tendency," i.e., a tendency to vary more widely than had previously been thought possible. This variation was, as always, within specific limits.[42]

In his appearance before the Evangelical Alliance, Dawson enlarged on this view:

> A new law is . . . coming into view. . . . It is that species, when first introduced, have an innate power of expansion, which enables them rapidly to extend themselves to the limits of their geographical range, and also to reach the limit of their divergence into races. These limits once reached, the races run on in parallel lines until they one by one run out and disappear.[43]

Dawson was very optimistic about the prospects for validating this law.

When questioned from the floor by Charles Hodge concerning the alleged atheism of Darwin's outlook, Dawson was also optimistic. He responded that, although Darwinism "logically leads to that conclusion, it was *not a result of scientific induction,* but a mere *hypothesis* [italics in text]." [44] Dawson remarked perceptively that Darwin was able to arrive at his conclusions by reasoning as to possibilities rather than facts. On this basis the combination of two possibilities gave a greater probability, whereas in ordinary logic such a procedure reduced probability.[45] Dawson assured his listeners that, when the discussion turned away from possibilities, the facts were "not otherwise explicable by the doctrine of creation." [46] He asked indulgence for the evolutionist who was, he said, "often a very

42 *Ibid.*

43 Philip Schaff and S. Irenaeus Prime (eds.), *History Essays, Orations, and Other Documents of the Sixth General Conference of the Evangelical Alliance* (New York, 1874), p. 274.

44 *Ibid.*, p. 320.

45 For a detailed elaboration of Darwin's use of the "logic of possibility," see Himmelfarb, *Darwin and the Darwinian Revolution,* pp. 273–276.

46 Schaff and Prime, *History . . . of the Sixth General Conference of the Evangelical Alliance,* p. 320.

darkened soul, struggling for light," driven to his infidelity "by the follies and inconsistencies of Christians." [47]

Scientific infidelity also occupied much of Dawson's attention in *The Story of the Earth and Man,* his final thrust at evolution in 1873.[48] In this book Dawson gave the most detailed statement to date of his views on evolution. His talents as a popularizer were indisputable and *The Story of the Earth and Man* was very widely circulated. For that matter, it remains a very readable book.

Dawson began with a consideration of the theories of evolution held by the ancient Greeks. Just as he was for a long time unable to distinguish Darwin from Lamarck, so he was unable, or unwilling, to delineate modern ideas of evolution from those of the Greeks. The current enthusiasm for evolution, he said, represented a recrudescence of "the crudest and most uncritical attempts of the human mind to grasp the system of nature." [49] The tremendous accumulation of scientific information since the eighteenth century had outstripped the scientist's capacity for proper generalizations; the result was the wild theorizing which currently afflicted sound science.

Whatever gloom Dawson may have suffered on this score was quickly overshadowed by the social catastrophe that he expected to follow close upon the heels of evolutionary speculations. The dangerous tendencies inherent in evolution, he thought, "must, before they disappear, descend to the lower strata, and reproduce themselves in grosser forms." "Grosser forms" for Dawson meant a general hedonism and, above all, "a welcome deliverance from all scruples of conscience." "In the domain

[47] *Ibid.,* p. 275.

[48] J. W. Dawson, *The Story of the Earth and Man* (New York, 1874). The book was brought out in Montreal in 1873 by B. Dawson (no relation); Harper's published it the following year. I have been unable to obtain a copy of the Montreal edition.

[49] *Ibid.,* p. 317.

of science," he hinted darkly, "evolutionism has like tendencies." [50]

In Dawson's opinion, it was fortunate for the children of light that such a menacing point of view rested on such a shaky foundation. He placed great emphasis on the fact that in 1873, some fourteen years after the publication of *The Origin of Species,* even the most ardent Darwinian was unwilling to assert that his case rested on facts actually observed; no one had ever observed an example of speciation. Similarly, much had been made of the support tendered to evolution by uniformitarian geology. However, Dawson was prompt to point out, uniformitarianism posited the extension into the past of phenomena currently observable; on this basis, he said, one must project into the past stable, immutable species. The sole evidence for evolution, said Dawson, was its ability "to account hypothetically for certain relations of living creatures to each other." [51]

This hypothetical nature of Darwinian thought was the basis of a lengthy discussion by Dawson of the by then notorious "gaps" in nature, e.g., between the organic and the inorganic, plant and animal, and, of course, species and other species. The enthusiasm of some evolutionists had led them to posit an unbroken chain of descent from man to the atom.[52] On this count, Dawson again linked evolution with the discredited quackery of the past. Nothing had been advanced, he asserted, to show any convincing evidence of a link between the organic and the inorganic. Sensational announcements of the artificial production of low forms of life occurred again and again, but in every case proved groundless.[53]

[50] *Ibid.*

[51] *Ibid.*, p. 322.

[52] In emphasizing this issue, Dawson was, for a change, a trifle ahead of his time, since John Tyndall's "Belfast Address" and the ensuing storm of controversy did not take place until a few months later.

[53] *Ibid.*, p. 326.

Although the gap between the organic and the inorganic was (and is) perhaps the most fiercely contested, it was not a matter of concern to Darwin; the greatest of the evolutionists was always willing to grant "one primordial form." The next gap, however, that between plant and animal, involved Darwin extensively. He later wrote three books that dealt with functions of plants that were on the border of animal activity: *The Movements and Habits of Climbing Plants* (1875), *Insectivorous Plants* (1875), and *The Power of Movement in Plants* (1881).[54]

Dawson contended that, so far, all attempts to show derivation of animals from plants had failed. Only in reproduction or decay did the function of plants resemble significantly those of animals. As with "spontaneous generation" and the artificial production of life, close analysis revealed that alleged cases of links between the animal and vegetable kingdoms were faulty. As far as Dawson was concerned, the only way to bridge this gap was to appeal to ignorance; if there was no evidence for a link between plants and animals, neither was there any positive evidence against such a link.[55]

The third and most important gap which challenged the evolutionist was that between particular species. Despite the "great work" of Darwin, said Dawson, this gap yawned as wide as ever. No case of derivation had ever been ascertained. Despite all efforts at artificial breeding, "the essential characters" of species remained unchanged. Even minor characteristics, he claimed, were often persistent. "The barriers established in nature between species . . . seem to be absolute." [56]

These controverted gaps were so readily considered barriers by Dawson because he found the creationist analysis

[54] Sir Gavin de Beer, *Charles Darwin* (New York, 1964), p. 249.

[55] Dawson, *The Story of the Earth and Man,* pp. 326–327.

[56] *Ibid.,* pp. 327–328.

thoroughly convincing. His idea of creationism was a very flexible one, so flexible that one wonders why it could not have been stretched just a bit more to include the derivation of species. For example, Dawson made very clear that by creation he did not mean a sudden bolt of lightning from the void that left a fully grown *Brontosaurus* at the point of impact. He accepted "creation by law" and was willing to grant that this did "not even exclude evolution or derivation to a certain extent." "Creation and derivation may, rightly understood, be complementary to each other." [57] He pointed out that even Darwin insisted on special creation of one primitive form of life. The creationist, he said, was in no worse position than most evolutionists; the former simply posited a greater number of creations.

As a special creationist, Dawson himself tended to minimize the number of creations. He had crossed swords with Agassiz fifteen years earlier over the incredibility of the number of creations demanded by the great Harvard scientist. Dawson's opinion was the same as that expressed by Sir Charles Lyell in a letter to him:

> I confess that Agassiz's last work drove me far over into Darwin's camp, or the Lamarckian view, for when he attributed the original of every race of man to an independent starting point, or act of creation, . . . I could not help thinking Lamarck must be right, for the rejection of his system led to such license.[58]

Dawson did not insist on special creation for every form labeled "species" by taxonomists. He noted that clear specific distinctions between closely related forms were often very difficult to find. Since no one denied that species were in many cases extremely variable, the absence of clear distinctions posed no problem to the creationist. Dawson,

[57] *Ibid.*, p. 341.

[58] Katherine M. Lyell (ed.), *Life, Letters and Journals of Sir Charles Lyell, Bart.* (London, 1881) 2: p. 331.

himself, was even willing to accept natural selection as a dominant factor in variation. He drew the line only at what he called "specific types." These "types" were marked by unquestionable distinctions on a level of importance that could only be termed specific. In Dawson's opinion "specific types" were the only forms in nature that had been specially created. Larger entities such as genera and families were simply convenient taxonomical categories; smaller entities, variations and many forms commonly regarded as species, Dawson recognized as mediate creations which might well be subject to evolutionary change.

It seems at first glance that Dawson was very reasonable on these points. However, what appears to be great flexibility is more accurately described as tactical retreat; to continue the military metaphor, Dawson shortened his lines. By arguing the case for a special creation on the basis of "specific types," Dawson removed from the discussion precisely those forms that were most relevant—the borderline cases. This tactic also made all of the many difficulties encountered by scientists in determining precise specific limits work against evolution. By restricting his creationism to "specific types," Dawson widened the gap between forms; he was in effect requiring the evolutionist to show derivation on a level somewhere between species and genera. Those areas where it was easiest to show transmutation were, therefore, preempted in advance, leaving only the very difficult task of bridging the wide gaps between clear and distinct types. The final and greatest advantage of this tactic for Dawson was that it enabled him to concede an enormous amount of random selection, while retaining his cherished notion of design. In sum, Dawson gave little to gain much.

The alternating sanctimony and ferocity of Dawson's attacks on evolution aroused the considerable abilities of

Asa Gray. According to his biographer and editor, A. Hunter Dupree, Gray saw in Dawson:

an opponent whose kind was not prominent thirteen years earlier [i.e., when Gray first began his heroic efforts on Darwin's behalf]—the convinced and close-minded anti-Darwinian scientist who based his career on orthodox Christianity . . . J. W. Dawson was a worthy man and in his day a useful scientist, but his "Story of Earth and Man" [*sic*] aroused Gray's disputative talents to the fullest.[59]

In the years between 1873 and 1875 Gray and Dawson clashed a number of times in print and in several private letters. Dawson sent Gray a copy of *The Story of the Earth and Man* as a gift in April of 1873.[60] Gray reviewed the book the following October in *The Nation.*

Gray identified Dawson as one of only two "good and eminent" scientists who held to the "entire fixity of species."[61] A popular book such as *The Story of the Earth and Man,* Gray conceded, rendered Dawson "rather more than less amenable to the criticisms we may be disposed to make of it." Gray also admitted that, despite this handicap, Dawson maintained the creationist position "with earnestness, much variety of argument and illustration, and no small ability."[62] The Harvard botanist found Dawson's scientific remarks respectable but out of date; however, Dawson's "vehemence and looseness of statement" irritated him. Gray protested the use of such phrases as "scientific banditti" and "outrages on common sense." Dawson's unjustified deprecation of his opponents was accompanied, in Gray's judgment, by an equation of opposition to special creation with atheism. He warned that

[59] Asa Gray, *Darwiniana,* ed. A. Hunter Dupree (Cambridge, Mass., 1963), p. 18.

[60] Dawson to Gray, April 17, 1873, Gray papers.

[61] Gray, *Darwiniana,* pp. 202–203. The other scientist was not named but the context of Gray's remark clearly implies "American scientist" and it is probable that he meant Louis Agassiz.

[62] *Ibid.*

this uncompromising line was a dangerous one. Men like Dawson were "more zealous than wise . . . [in firing] away in their catapults the very bastions of the citadel, in defence of outposts that have become untenable." It was always possible, said Gray, to take this hard line, but far more reasonable to take a theistic view.[63]

Dawson and Gray came into conflict again over the latter's address, "Sequoia and Its History," as departing president of the American Association for the Advancement of Science in 1872.[64] This was concerned with the "Laramie Question." This puzzling problem, which was to bedevil geologists for decades, arose when one of the reports of the United States Geological Survey for 1872 included conflicting data on the geologic age of large portions of western America. The paleobotanist Leo Lesquereux was convinced that the sedimentary rocks containing the fossils were formed during the early Cenozoic. Frederick B. Meek and Edward Drinker Cope were equally certain that the animal remains were late Mesozoic.[65]

Without taking sides in the controversy, Asa Gray was quick to see the significance for evolution of the new fossil discoveries. For an evolutionist such as Gray, the mixed fossil remains provided a chance to study a transition from one population to another without violent change. In his address to the A.A.A.S., he developed the links between the early Cenozoic and an earlier and similar flora in the Arctic and northeastern Japan. According to Gray, the record plainly indicated that the American plants had evolved from northern predecessors.[66]

Dawson, as might have been expected, read the record in a different light. He wrote to Gray in the spring fol-

[63] *Ibid.*, p. 206.

[64] *Ibid.*, pp. 169–194.

[65] For a full account of the "Laramie Question," see George P. Merrill, *The First One Hundred Years of American Geology* (New Haven, 1924), pp. 579–593.

[66] Gray, *Darwiniana*, pp. 192–193.

lowing the address to express his dissent. The wide geographical distribution of *Sequoia* referred to by Gray did not show evolution in Dawson's opinion:

> I have no objection to species of Sequoia . . . travelling . . . to Greenland or China; but . . . I think they would still be the same species, not modified except varietally.[67]

Dawson explored the "Laramie Question" himself in his presidential address to the Natural History Society of Montreal in 1874. For him the conflicting testimony of the fossils offered a test of whether organisms were introduced by "a slow and gradual evolution of new types by descent with modification" or "abundantly and in perfection at once." [68] Dawson interpreted the sudden appearance of the Cenozoic flora in the middle of very slow physical change as evidence that this flora was either specially created or had existed somewhere for an extremely long period of time. Neither alternative, he said, offered much for evolution. If one chose the latter, the rate of change in Gray's Sequoias between the early Cenozoic and the present was so slow that, projected back into the past, it made the derivation of such plants simply unreasonable. For Dawson, the early Cenozoic flora of western America, like the Devonian flora of eastern America, showed the appearance of many species without predecessors and the extinction of many others without successors.

Gray vigorously disputed Dawson's conclusions. In a review of Dawson's address for the *American Journal of Science,* he objected again to the slurs cast on Dawson's opponents. More to the point, he accused Dawson of quibbling over the question of specific or varietal change. Wherever intermediate forms existed, Dawson termed the differences between predecessor and successor "varietal." Where no intermediate forms existed, he claimed positive

[67] Dawson to Gray, March 26, 1873, Gray papers.

[68] *The Canadian Naturalist and Quart. Jour. of Science* 7 (1874): pp. 286–287.

proof of special creation. Gray quoted Harrington's famous couplet:

> Treason doth never prosper, what's the reason?
> Why, if it prosper, none dare call it treason.

According to Gray, Dawson was saying, in effect, "species never evolve, for if they evolve, they are not species." [69]

Following this last exchange with Gray, Dawson gave a series of lectures at Union Theological Seminary and Princeton University. The lectures were published in 1875 under the title of *Nature and the Bible.* He could not have paid much heed to Gray's admonitions, for in *Nature and the Bible* he applied to modern scientists Christ's words to the Sadducees: "Ye do err, not knowing the Scriptures, nor the power of God." It is doubtful whether Gray would have been mollified by Dawson's qualifying remark that Christ always preferred the Sadducees to the Pharisees, i.e., honest ignorance to religious hypocrisy.[70] *Nature and the Bible* dealt primarily with the general relation of science to religion and more specifically with the old Genesis-geology controversy; however, Dawson included two chapters on evolution.

Most of the evolution material in *Nature and the Bible* restated Dawson's previous position. He again put forth the views on "creation by law" that he had advanced at the conference of the Evangelical Alliance. He asserted once more that paleontology stood squarely in the path of the commonly held view of evolution. Most evolutionists claimed slow, inexorable change from lower to higher forms; paleontology, said Dawson, had established the rapid introduction of species in many places at once. The new species were usually very highly developed and subsequently degraded rather than improved.[71]

69 *Amer. Jour. of Science,* 2nd ser., 8 (August, 1874): pp. 152–153.
70 J. W. Dawson, *Nature and the Bible* (New York, 1875), p. 185.
71 *Ibid.,* p. 143.

It was Dawson's custom to add references to new developments along with his repetition of earlier views. *Nature and the Bible* was no exception. The recent work of Huxley and Marsh on the horse sequence attracted Dawson's attention. The two evolutionists had made the nearest approach to direct paleontological evidence for evolution. Dawson, employing his standard tactic of using the opposition's strength against itself, asserted that the fact that they had come so near and yet had failed was a good indication that no one was ever going to make paleontology work for evolution.

True, Marsh and Huxley had shown a progressive chain of ancestry for the modern horse; however, even Cuvier had held to progression and progression was not derivation. The key element, according to Dawson, was the passage of one form into another and on this point Marsh and Huxley had failed to establish their case. Even if one granted this point to the Darwinians, the complicated combination of changes that was necessary for such a transmutation was "simply incredible, except on the supposition of intentional intervention." [72] The time had come, he said, to abandon "the brilliant fabric of speculation" erected by Darwin and "the enticing but unsubstantial" foundation of analogy. Dawson called for a return to a more inductive basis for biological theory.[73]

Dawson himself attempted an inductive survey of the basis for evolution a few months later at the meeting of the A.A.A.S. at Detroit. In 1875 he was serving as vice-president of the Association and as head of the Natural History Section. His vice-presidential address, "The Origin and History of Life on Our Planet," was a scathing survey of the deficiencies of the paleontological evidence for evolution.

[72] *Ibid.*, p. 144.
[73] *Ibid.*, pp. 240–241.

Dawson began with the earliest fossils, the problematical remains from the Precambrian. Not surprisingly, he based his case primarily on *Eozoön canadense*. He had labored long and hard to establish *Eozoön* as the greatest of all foraminiferal forms of life, both in magnitude and complexity. In his opinion, *Eozoön* was evidence of the early introduction of highly developed species, with subsequent degradation rather than improvement. The greatest significance of *Eozoön,* however, lay in the vast gap between it and other foraminifers—a gap that was inexplicable under any evolutionary hypothesis.[74]

Moving up to the early Cambrian, Dawson noted that species of trilobites had been found in Wales which scarcely differed from modern forms of arthropods. The same was true of many other forms. "The Lingulellae [brachiopods] . . . represent a peculiar and distinct type, handed down, through all the vicissitudes of the geological ages, to the present day." A similar case was that of *Leperditia,* a Paleozoic crustacean. Dawson cited *Plutonia* (a synonym for the Cambrian trilobite *Paradoxides*); he asked his listeners to suppose that they had a living specimen of *Plutonia* in front of them, "flapping vigorously its great tail, and full of life and energy." *Plutonia* furnished a repetition of the *Eozoön* case, said Dawson. On an evolutionary basis, there was no "solution . . . to the appearance of these early forms of life." [75] The paleontological record told the same tale as it advanced to recent times: on the one hand early and rapid introduction of highly advanced forms (*Eozoön,* the Cambrian trilobites, the Devonian flora); on the other, a marked persistence of type (Lingulellae, several species of clams, *Leperditia,* and the land shells of Madeira).

[74] J. W. Dawson, "Vice President's Address," *Proc. Amer. Assoc. Advancement of Science* 24 (1875): pp. b10–b11.

[75] *Ibid.*, pp. b11–b13.

Facts such as these, Dawson asserted, showed that current theories of evolution were "fundamentally defective." These theories tended "to refer numerous and complex phenomena to one cause," while the evidence indicated at the very least that "many concurrent forces" were at work. Evolutionists in general made unwarranted use of analogy. Dawson objected especially to the equation of the analogical method used by uniformitarian geologists with the evolutionists' use of the alleged analogy between individual embryonic development and specific derivation. Those who advanced these crude analogies as evidence for evolution were ignoring "the vastly varied and correlated interdependencies of natural things and forces, and . . . the unity of plan which pervades the whole." [76]

Dawson's many books, articles, and public appearances in the 1870's established him as something of an anti-Darwinian celebrity. He began to receive numerous lecture invitations; in 1875 he gave the Phi Beta Kappa address at Harvard (in which he touched only incidentally on evolution). Dawson reviewed Darwin's *Insectivorous Plants* for *The International Review.* His analysis was straightforward and generally approving. He disagreed with Darwin only over the issue of design. He could not accept the notion that insect-eating plants had acquired their peculiar abilities through random selection as a means of gaining an advantage in the struggle to survive. Far from showing random selection, he argued, the insectivorous plants were outstanding examples of exactly the sort of detailed contrivance that could not occur by chance. In a very interesting philosophical aside Dawson disagreed with those who held that the theistic scientist must accept God's contrivance of death and destruction as well as his contrivance of intricate structures. A universe of material organisms was by definition subject to decay, he said; from the stand-

[76] *Ibid.,* pp. b19–b22.

point of natural theology, all one could expect was that death in nature be accomplished in the least painful manner. Where struggle existed in nature, its very thoroughness was, for Dawson, a proof of design![77]

Dawson had another opportunity to rebut a leading evolutionist in 1876, when T. H. Huxley came to the United States and delivered his famous New York lectures. Dawson was asked to rebut Huxley for Lyman Abbott and Henry Ward Beecher's periodical, *The Christian Union.* Abbott wrote to Dawson requesting "a critique on the lectures, written for popular readers rather than for professional students. . . . You could write with a perfectly free pen."[78]

Dawson's rebuttal, also printed in *The International Review,* coupled praise for Huxley with scorn for Huxley's ideas. Dawson's strategy was familiar: no more able spokesman for evolution could have been found:

> Huxley is an able, well-read, industrious, conscientious biologist, and has a boldness of utterance and an instinct in favor of fair dealing and equal rights, along with a genuine hatred of humbug and superstition.

The fact that, despite this ability, Huxley failed was evidence that the fault was in the theory.[79]

Huxley had classified the evidence for evolution into three categories: "neutral," "favorable," and "demonstrative."[80] Dawson challenged Huxley's terminology. The first two categories, he said, were euphemistic; under these headings Huxley brought forward "really formidable objections to evolution disguised as witnesses in its favor, in order that in this capacity they may be examined *pro forma*

[77] J. W. Dawson, "Insectivorous Plants," *International Rev.* 3 (1876): pp. 69–70.

[78] Lyman Abbott to Dawson, September 5, 1876, Dawson papers.

[79] J. W. Dawson, "Professor Huxley in New York," *International Rev.* 4 (January, 1877): p. 50.

[80] Thomas H. Huxley, *American Addresses* (New York, 1877), pp. 31, 71–73.

and dismissed."[81] Only Huxley's third category, "demonstrative," was regarded seriously by Dawson and the term he would have used for this evidence was "neutral."

The most important instance of "neutral" evidence advanced by Huxley himself was the phenomenon of persistence of type.[82] It was all well and good, in Dawson's opinion, to theorize about the perfect adaptation over the millions of years of organisms such as the Lingullelae; such theorizing did not get around the improbability involved in positing the evolution of species that burst suddenly onto the scene in the Cambrian period and did not change in all the time since. Special creation remained a more reasonable explanation of such phenomena. Huxley's appeal to the imperfection of the fossil record made no sense to Dawson, who objected to the aggressive use of undiscovered fossils. Dawson admitted the possibility that new discoveries might alter existing notions on the persistence of type. He thought, however, that such discoveries would be small comfort to Huxley; there was little probability that they would "explain why, after we had traced species back for vast periods of time, and over every kind of physical revolution, they should at some antecedent period begin to change if we could only trace them further."[83] As far as discovery was concerned, the future belonged to no one; new discoveries might well show that evolution was a pipe-dream. In the meantime, persistence of type, far from being "neutral" evidence, was a stumbling block to the theory. To classify such evidence as "neutral" was, in Dawson's judgment, "certainly drawing largely on our credulity."[84]

The second category of evidence, classified as "favorable" according to Huxley, was based on the general na-

[81] Dawson, "Professor Huxley in New York," p. 41.
[82] Huxley, *American Addresses,* pp. 39–41.
[83] Dawson, "Professor Huxley in New York," p. 42.
[84] *Ibid.,* p. 43.

ture of the fossil record. Huxley argued that paleontologists were regularly finding fossils which narrowed the gaps between living forms—intercalary forms. These were "favorable" evidence, he said, because they were just what one would expect if the hypothesis of evolution were true.[85] Dawson challenged this line of reasoning on the ground that many of the fossil series revealed by paleontology were not consecutive in time. Organisms which, in an evolutionary framework, should have preceded certain species often occurred at the same time or even much later. Most of the fossil record showed no indication of genealogical descent; far from offering "favorable" evidence, it was a major obstacle for evolution.[86]

Huxley's "demonstrative" evidence met this last objection of Dawson. Huxley cited those portions of the paleontological record in which succesive geological formations contained organic remains which showed progressive development, making the possibility of genealogical descent a very real one. The burden of his case rested on the famous horse sequence. While all existing horses in America were descendants of horses brought over from Europe, the remains of many horselike animals were to be found in the great fossil beds of the West. Recent deposits contained fossil horses very closely related to the European species from which modern American horses had been bred. The American Pliocene contained the remains of *Pliohippus,* an animal very similar to the modern horse. Like its contemporary relative, *Pliohippus* had one toe; however, it also had two splint bones which seemed to be remnants of two additional toes. The next fossil in the sequence, *Protohippus,* showed that the splint bones were in fact partial toes. Further back, in the Miocene, *Miohippus* and *Mesohippus* possessed three full toes and a rudimentary

[85] Huxley, *American Addresses,* pp. 46–48, 67.
[86] Dawson, "Professor Huxley in New York," p. 43.

fourth. Finally, the oldest fossil then known in the sequence, *Orohippus,* from the Eocene, showed four full toes. According to Huxley, other structural elements in the fossil sequence revealed similar gradations.[87]

This elaborate sequence, so persuasive to so many nineteenth-century observers, made little impression on Dawson. He recognized that the evidence for a correlation between succession in time and anatomical changes was good. The evidence for a genetic connection, he asserted, was less convincing. The different stages in the sequence were separated by vast intervals of time and by important structural differences. Dawson noted perceptively that the same method of argument would prove the direct descent of modern American horses from those whose bones lay in Professor Marsh's cabinet; yet everyone knew that this was not the case.[88]

Dawson also found fault with Huxley's interpretation of the horse sequence at its lowest rung, *Orohippus* (*Hyracotherium* had not been recognized as an ancestor of the modern horse). Huxley neglected to mention, he said, the difficulties involved in finding an ancestor for *Orohippus.* Using the rate of change between *Orohippus* and the modern horse, Dawson argued again that any predecessor for *Orohippus* must have lived further back in geological time than any known placental mammal—further back even than any likely ancestor of such a mammal. *Orohippus,* for Dawson, was like the Cambrian trilobites, the Devonian fishes and the "air breathers" of the Carboniferous; it had no credible predecessor and, thus, posed a serious challenge to evolution.[89]

The wide acceptance of Huxley's conversion of liabilities into assets was incomprehensible to Dawson. It sur-

87 Huxley, *American Addresses,* pp. 87–90.
88 Dawson, "Professor Huxley in New York," p. 45.
89 *Ibid.,* p. 47.

prised him even more that many people were influenced not only by what he regarded as a feeble case, but by analogies erected on the basis of this case. Dawson, himself not averse to the occasional use of spectacular analogies, protested most strongly in the case of man: "if our horses can be made daily to trot out before us their descent from Orohippus, we may by and by be induced to admit a similar origin for their grooms and their riders." [90]

Dawson saw the horse sequence as a sort of Waterloo for evolution. Here, he said, according to one of its greatest exponents, was the best paleontological evidence of derivation; yet both the evidence and the edifice of analogy failed to stand up under scrutiny. "Evolution," he concluded, "will have its day, and then men will wonder how they could have believed it." [91]

Unfortunately for Dawson, the New York lectures had none of the finality of a Waterloo. Dawson's review was just one more round in a struggle that was to last until his death. His next effort was a series of six articles for Charles Hodge's *Princeton Review*. Published over a three-year period, these articles were largely devoted to a reassertion of Dawson's stock arguments; however, three of them emphasized rebuttal of recent evolutionist publications.

The first of the articles, "Evolution and the Apparition of Animal Forms," was published in May of 1878. Dawson's creationist outlook was evident in the title; animal forms, he said, did not develop or evolve; they "appeared," suddenly and inexplicably.[92] For the first time, Dawson employed the argument against natural selection based on the many examples of gratuitous beauty in nature. He

[90] *Ibid.*, p. 37.

[91] *Ibid.*, p. 48.

[92] J. W. Dawson, "Evolution and the Apparition of Animal Forms," *Princeton Rev.* 1 (May, 1878): p. 662.

cited specifically the "Venus Flower-Basket." No one confronted with

> all this unity and variety, mechanical contrivance and varied beauty, associated with so little of vitality and complexity in the . . . organisms concerned, could doubt for a moment the action of a creative intelligence in the initiation of such phenomena.[93]

In Dawson's opinion, nature was characterized by forms that could not have occurred through random selection. In addition to gratuitous beauty, there was the intricate structure of the eyes. He noted that Paleozoic paleontology revealed two types of eyes: one composed of many parts radiating from one center, the other consisting of a single, complex structure capable of a wide range of adjustment. Both types, he said, were perfected very early in the Paleozoic Era, during the Cambrian period. The first type was represented by the ever-useful trilobites; the second by ancient cuttlefish. According to Dawson, the two types of eyes were so different that neither could have given birth to the other and, more important, neither could have produced a third, and later, type of eye—that found in the fishes of the Upper Silurian and Devonian.[94] "Such facts as these . . . remove the origin of eyes very far from the domain of spontaneous development."[95]

The second significant article by Dawson for *The Princeton Review* was a vigorous attack on Ernst Haeckel, author of *The Evolution of Man.* Dawson found in Haeckel's work the quintessence of all he objected to in evolution. Haeckel's almost exclusive reliance on analogy particularly aroused him. He accused Haeckel of a type of deceit in persistently implying more than the evidence warranted. Haeckel, said Dawson, was in the habit of describing "the embryo of a fish or an amphibian, and as

[93] *Ibid.*, p. 670.
[94] *Ibid.*, pp. 672–673.
[95] *Ibid.*, p. 674.

we become more interested in the curious details, it is suddenly by some clever phrase transformed into a reptile or bird." [96]

When Haeckel cited specific examples of intermediate forms, Dawson was equally critical. In describing the lancelet, *Amphioxus,* he noted that Haeckel was careful to point out that it differed more from ordinary fishes than a fish did from a man. "Before we are aware the lancelet is gone and a fish is in its place, and this fish has the potency to become a man in due time." If one ignored this sleight of hand, he asserted, one could readily see that *Amphioxus* was intermediate in some respects between fishes and mollusks or worms, but so far from either that it actually marked a great gap between each of these forms. Haeckel's trick was to make the gap appear to be a stepping-stone.[97]

Dawson made an effective attack on Haeckel's renowned Law of Recapitulation; "ontogeny recapitulates phylogeny." Phylogenesis, according to Dawson, was not a process open to observation; even the possibility of phylogenesis remained to be proved. This much was known, however—"the very causes on which it must depend are altogether different from those at work in ontogenesis." Furthermore, it was a simple fact of observation that many ontogenetic characteristics did not correspond with any known phylogeny.[98]

Haeckel's use of linguistic analogy also drew fire from Dawson. The argument for derivation of species based on the derivation of language was nonsensical in Dawson's opinion. Language had been known to change; species had not. Individual languages had been traced to a common ancestor and, in many cases, the connecting links were unbroken. No such evidence could be adduced for specific

[96] J. W. Dawson, "Haeckel on the Evolution of Man," *Princeton Rev.* 5 (May, 1880): p. 448.

[97] *Ibid.*

[98] *Ibid.*, pp. 449–450.

derivation. The paleontological record still weighed heavily against evolution, said Dawson. Common ancestors and connecting links had not been found. Haeckel's analogy, then, had relevance only if one assumed a common ancestor, the existence of which, after all, was precisely the point at issue.[99]

Haeckel's position was an extreme one and there seems little question that he stretched the limits of analogy beyond recognition. He was consequently an easy target for Dawson, as easy as Dawson himself was for a man like Asa Gray. Perhaps realizing the strength of his case against Haeckel, Dawson attempted to convict more reasonable evolutionists by association. He asserted that Haeckel's materialism and irreligion should be a good lesson to the religious fellow travelers of evolution, men such as Count Saporta, Joseph Leconte, Jean Gaudry, and St. George Mivart. He doubted "whether they can maintain this position [theistic evolution] against the monists, and whether they will be able in the end to retain any practical form of religion." [100]

One prominent theistic evolutionist who was not named by Dawson was his erstwhile antagonist, Asa Gray. Gray wrote to Dawson to praise the article on Haeckel, which he termed "excellent." He questioned Dawson's appropriation of paleontology for exclusively anti-evolutionary use. He also registered a protest against Dawson's disparagement of theistic evolution:

> You would do a real service if you would address yourself to the gist of the question and give your reasons why "they cannot maintain this position against the monists," i.e., why their position against the monists is not as good as yours.[101]

[99] *Ibid.*, p. 453.
[100] *Ibid.*, pp. 460–461.
[101] Asa Gray to Dawson, May 10, 1880, Dawson papers.

The final important article in *The Princeton Review* was a lengthy review of Alfred Russel Wallace's *Island Life.* The acrimonious tone of portions of Dawson's article on Haeckel was in marked contrast to his balanced treatment of Wallace. Although he was not prepared to accept the latter's evolutionism, Dawson found the co-discoverer of natural selection a very congenial adversary. *Island Life* was a formidable attempt to explore variation in isolated but proximate populations. Wallace extended to book length some of Darwin's earlier speculations on the evolutionary relevance of life on isolated islands such as the Galapagos and the Azores.

Dawson began with his standard tactic of using against Wallace the very evidence most crucial to the evolutionist case. Wallace proposed evolution as the only reasonable explanation of the distribution of insular flora and fauna; Dawson countered by arguing that so far was "evolution from being a key to distribution that the whole question would become much more simple if this element were omitted altogether." [102] In his opinion, a deeper knowledge of the geological aspects of oceanic islands would have served Wallace better than evolution.

In addition to geological deficiencies, Dawson protested what he regarded as a misinterpretation of the observed facts. None of the islands considered by Wallace contained an autochthnous population, i.e., a population that had originated on the islands themselves. In each case the population originated elsewhere. In addition, even those islands which were the longest colonized and were furthest from possible sources of population contained no evidence of significant modifications in their inhabitants since colonization.[103]

[102] J. W. Dawson, "Continental and Island Life: Their Present State and Past History," *Princeton Rev.* 8 (July, 1881): p. 16.

[103] *Ibid.*

In *Island Life,* Wallace had been concerned with practically all of the important islands in the world: Borneo, Java, Bermuda, Formosa, New Zealand, Madagascar, the Celebes, the Azores, the Galapagos—even Great Britain. Faced with the space limitation of an article, Dawson considered only two of these in any detail, the Azores and the Galapagos.

According to Dawson, the first of these, the Azores, contained only one indigenous mammal, a bat which was "identical with a European species and no doubt reached the islands by flight." [104] There were no indigenous reptiles, amphibians, or fresh-water fish. Of the eighteen species of birds that could be regarded as permanent residents, fifteen were common European or African species; two more were found in Madeira and the Canaries and "therefore may reasonably be supposed to have been derived from Africa." The only bird that could be regarded as peculiar to the Azores was a bullfinch, "so nearly related to the European bullfinch that it may be regarded as merely a local variety." The land plants of the Azores were almost wholly identical with existing European and African species.[105]

Wallace accounted for this evidence of specific stability by arguing that the glacial cold had destroyed most life on the Azores and that nearly all of the contemporary organisms were relatively recent arrivals which had not had time to evolve further. Thus, their apparent stability did not seriously challenge evolution.[106] This was an inadequate explanation for Dawson who pointed out that there was little probability that the glacial refrigeration had been sufficiently severe to depopulate the Azores. The evidence, in his judgment, pointed to immense time and al-

[104] *Ibid.,* p. 17.
[105] *Ibid.,* pp. 16–17.
[106] Alfred Russel Wallace, *Island Life* (New York, 1881), pp. 239–240.

most no change, a very different prospect for evolutionary theory.

Dawson admitted that Wallace was on much firmer ground in discussing the Azorean beetles, "a few quite distinct from any elsewhere known." He was forced into the rather weak position of arguing that knowledge of continental beetles was incomplete and that the species in question were "small and obscure." He responded rather feebly to Wallace's evolutionary interpretation of the beetles with the suggestion that they were unmodified survivors of beetles that were now extinct on the mainland.[107]

Dawson thought that there was some evidence for the latter hypothesis in the land snails of the Azores. Of sixty-nine species of land snails on the islands, thirty-two were "peculiar, tho nearly all are closely allied to European types." Admitting for the sake of argument that all thirty-two were genuine species, Dawson maintained that it was not improbable that Miocene or Pliocene species had migrated to the Azores. Although these islands had thus far yielded no fossil land snails, many Pliocene snails had been found on Madeira and Porto Santo. Several of the Madeira fossils, while differing from modern European snails, were very similar to European Miocene snails. Madeira, then, provided evidence not of derivation but of preservation of species which had been long extinct in Europe. "May we not infer," Dawson asked, "that the same was the case in the Azores?" [108]

Dawson's own answer to this rhetorical question was to apply the hypothesis to other islands, notably St. Helena and the Galapagos. Life on St. Helena, he said, showed very old forms—"early Tertiary, even Secondary." However, it was the Galapagos, so important to Darwin's research, that most interested Dawson. The Canadian pale-

[107] Dawson, "Continental and Island Life," p. 17.
[108] *Ibid.*, p. 18.

ontologist contended that Darwin might have come to very different conclusions had he been aware of what was now known about the relation between geological history and distribution. Much of the fauna of the Galapagos, according to Dawson, resembled that of the Mesozoic or early Cenozoic eras. The Galapagos birds, for example, represented "to our modern eyes the unmodified descendants of continental birds of the early Tertiary." [109]

The most dramatic evidence for evolution obtained by Darwin and Wallace from the Galapagos was the presence of many different but closely related species on neighboring islands. Dawson's rebuttal to this argument was the familiar assertion that the alleged species were, in fact, merely varieties.[110]

Dawson thought that geological considerations explained the alleged Mesozoic and early Cenozoic character of Galapagos life far more effectively than the hypothesis of evolution. Darwin had commented on the lack of color in both the plants and animals of the islands.[111] This phenomenon was especially curious since the islands were near the equator, a region characterized by luxuriant color. Dawson's explanation of this absence of color was that the same lack of color characterized North American plants and birds. The Galapagos, he claimed, were populated at a time when a strait separated North and South America, allowing ocean currents to drift through and bring the drab life of North America to a new home on the equator, "where they have been emprisoned ever since." Such an explanation of the origin and antiquity of the flora and fauna of the Galapagos rendered "unnecessary any hypothesis of modification." [112]

[109] *Ibid.*, p. 20.

[110] *Ibid.*, pp. 21–22.

[111] Charles Darwin, *Journal of Researches into the Natural History and Geology of the Countries Visited During the Voyage of the H.M.S. Beagle* (New York, 1846) 2: pp. 140, 149–150.

[112] Dawson, "Continental and Island Life," p. 21.

Dawson's *Princeton Review* articles were his last major contributions to the evolution controversy. Large portions of four of his subsequent books, *The Chain of Life in Geological Time* (1880), *The Geological History of Plants* (1888), *The Meeting Place of Geology and History* (1895), and *Eden Lost and Won* (1895), were devoted to evolution, but these consisted entirely of restatements of the classic anti-evolutionary arguments: early appearance of advanced forms, persistence of type, gratuitous beauty, gaps in the paleontological record, the inability of natural selection to originate favorable variations, and the tendency of struggle to degrade; in short, all of the arguments that Dawson had been using, along with other critics, since 1860.

These critics were legion, but, for sheer volume of words, Dawson may well have been the most active opponent of evolution. On a qualitative basis, Dawson's crusade against evolution is more difficult to appraise. It was at once futile, valid, respectable, and just plain cranky. However, nineteenth-century evolutionists by no means had all of the answers to questions such as those raised by Dawson. If his attribution of the death of God to the new outlook was hysterical and a bit premature, his protest against the ability of natural selection alone to account for the origin of variations was valid. Similarly, the paleontological record belonged to neither side in the nineteenth century and Dawson's anti-evolutionary interpretation was respectable on most counts. The rough treatment he occasionally handed out to his opponents was deplorable, to be sure, but in his calmer moments Dawson regretted his excesses of language. The spirit of the controversy was not always conducive to moderation and in this respect Dawson was rather restrained when compared with Huxley, Tyndall, or even Louis Agassiz. Ultimately, the significance of men like Dawson rests in the stimulus they provided for further study. They also serve who oppose.

# *VI. The Eozoön Controversy*[1]

Eozoön canadense, "the dawn animal of Canada," was found in the Precambrian rocks of eastern Canada in 1858. The discovery startled the geological world, since at the time few paleontologists believed that such metamorphic rocks could preserve fossils or even that life could have existed so long ago. In fact, what we now call Precambrian was then commonly designated by the term Azoic, i.e., lifeless. It is not surprising, then, that the authenticity of *Eozoön canadense* was disputed. The ensuing controversy lasted for nearly fifty years and developed into one of the most contentious issues in nineteenth-century geology.[1]

While the inorganic nature of *Eozoön* has long been established and *Eozoön* is no longer of scientific interest, the controversy has significance for the history of science. It provides an example of the manner in which every aspect of nineteenth-century paleontology was scrutinized for its bearing on evolution. It is also a classic case of the confrontation of younger specialists with each other and with the older generation of broadly trained "naturalists."

There were two main reasons for the persistence of the dispute. Most obvious and most important was the inability of early paleontology to settle the matter. The second reason, seldom stated by the disputants, was the significance of *Eozoön* in the larger issue of derivation of species. For, were *Eozoön* proved to be organic, evolutionists would be confronted with the most impressive of all gaps in the paleontological record, a gap that would

[1] For a full discussion of the *Eozoön* controversy, see Charles F. O'Brien, "*Eozoön Canadense,* the Dawn Animal of Canada," *Isis* **61** (Summer, 1970): pp. 206–223.

give pause to even the most ardent evolutionist. On the other hand, if this gap was successfully explained or overcome by the finding of subsequent forms related to *Eozoön,* the evolutionists could rejoice in having found, at the earliest date of known animal life, the simplest form of life, a form reasonably akin to the "one primordial form" of Darwin's speculation. In short, there was something at stake for both sides in the greater scientific controversy.

*Eozoön* presented a difficult challenge. It occurred in rocks that were so old and so highly metamorphosed that paleontologists had previously doubted even the possibility of finding organic remains in them. Furthermore, the most ardent supporters of the organic origin of *Eozoön* admitted that their best specimens were so thoroughly altered that the details of organic structure were difficult to discern. On the other hand, when those who insisted that *Eozoön* was a mineral substance looked into their microscopes, they did not see even traces of organic structure. They saw instead a curiously regular arrangement of minerals; such an arrangement, they said, was unusual but not unprecedented. However, just as the supporters of *Eozoön* persistently failed to produce the unassailable specimen, the opponents were unable to establish any mineralogical sequence which could successfully explain the particular form and composition of *Eozoön.* In the absence of conclusive evidence on either side, the controversy dragged on for almost thirty years. It was not until the 1890's that the issue was decided in favor of the inorganic origin of *Eozoön.*

*Eozoön* was discovered by a collector for the Geological Survey of Canada in 1858. In the next few years, the director of the Survey, Sir William Logan, displayed the alleged fossil at several scientific meetings but found few geologists willing to accept *Eozoön* as organic. In 1864 he brought specimens to Dawson, who confirmed the presence of organic remains and identified the fossil as a giant foraminifer. When William B. Carpenter, a leading authority of Foraminifera, confirmed Dawson's opinion, widespread acceptance of the organic origin of *Eozoön* followed.

However, two Irish mineralogists, William King and Thomas H. Rowney, challenged this view. In an article published in 1866 "On the So-called 'Eozoonal Rock,'" they began a bitter controversy that lasted nearly fifty years. Their microscopic analyses led them to conclude that *Eozoön* was a mineral. They could find none of the traces of organic structure that others professed to see.

Dawson and Carpenter dismissed the mineralogical opponents of *Eozoön* rather casually—even impolitely. They generally denied King and Rowney's credentials to judge the presence or absence of foraminiferal remains. However, when a recognized Foraminifera specialist, Karl Möbius, pronounced in favor of the mineral origin of *Eozoön,* the level of dispute rose considerably. Möbius, a professor of zoology at Kiel, studied the very slide sections that had led Carpenter and Dawson to declare that *Eozoön* was a true fossil. His study, published in *Nature* in 1879, was a thorough, convincing attack on virtually every aspect of the Eozoönist case. His work settled the matter for a great many observers. However, Dawson responded by charging that Möbius was simply not competent to judge *Eozoön* because he was not sufficiently schooled in Precambrian geology.

Such unbecoming behavior of Dawson shows more than professional jealousy; it reveals that he believed the much larger issue of evolution was deeply involved in the *Eozoön* question.

Darwin had cited the discovery of *Eozoön* in the fourth edition of *The Origin of Species* as showing a succession of life from simpler to more complex and as revealing a longer duration for life on earth. This longer duration, of course, made natural selection a more plausible explanation for evolution. Darwin was also able to cite Dawson himself on the question of indirect evidence for more primitive predecessors of *Eozoön*.

This turn of events startled Dawson, who was throughout his life a vigorous opponent of Darwin. He countered this use of *Eozoön* with the statement that, far from providing paleontological evidence for evolution, the discovery of the controverted fossil revealed the grandest of all gaps in the record. There was no link whatever between *Eozoön* and any forms of the succeeding geological period, said Dawson. "Those evolutionists who have regarded the dawn-animal as an evidence in their favour have been obliged to have recourse to supposition and assumption." There was no evidence that *Eozoön* was defeated in a struggle for survival; it was merely "superseded" by other species.[2]

*Eozoön*'s testimony on Darwinism was not merely negative, according to Dawson. It was powerful evidence for the endurance of species. When we consider its endurance, "we acquire a most profound impression of the persistence of the lower forms of animal life, and know that mountains may be removed and continents swept away and replaced, before the least of the humble gelatinous Protozoa can finally perish." For Dawson, this was convincing evidence of the solicitude that God showed for all of His creatures. Since *Eozoön* was a gigantic foraminifer, far surpassing any modern species of Foraminifera in size, it taught us that lower forms may be introduced "in some of their grandest modifications as to form and complexity" and subsequently decay and degenerate. In Dawson's view *Eozoön* provided no evidence whatever of a higher form developing out of a lower, but, rather, indicated precisely the opposite.[3]

[2] Dawson, *Life's Dawn on Earth* (London, 1875), pp. 227–229.
[3] *Ibid.*, pp. 224–225, 231.

A primary reason for the long duration of the controversy was the inability of anti-Eozoönists to produce a convincing mineralogical explanation of the peculiar form of *Eozoön*. A major step in this direction was taken in 1894 when J. W. Gregory and Hugh Johnston-Lavis produced evidence that *Eozoön* occurred in ejected blocks of limestone in the area of Mount Vesuvius. A fossil shot out of a volcano was a phenomenon few were prepared to accept! The specimens of *Eozoön* found near Vesuvius had been formed very recently, from a geological standpoint, and the causes were known—great heat and pressure on limestone. The Vesuvius *Eozoön* had the advantage of being, for practical purposes, a laboratory-produced specimen.

Dawson was not daunted, however; he argued that the Vesuvius specimens were not *Eozoön*. He wrote a number of letters and notes to *The Geological Magazine* challenging Gregory and Johnston-Lavis. He lectured on Precambrian paleontology at the Lowell Institute in Boston during December of 1895. His lectures were published in book form with the title *Relics of Primeval Life*. In these lectures he reviewed again the evidence for the organic origin of *Eozoön* and cited the recent work of C. D. Walcott of the United States Geological Survey as showing that *Eozoön* was not alone, that there were several indisputable fossils of similar age. Dawson speculated that, a generation hence, there would be no reason to question *Eozoön* because of its isolation from the fossils of the Cambrian and Silurian. These discoveries, while they may have served to make the organic *Eozoön* more credible, precluded further use of the alleged fossil against evolution. Dawson was working on still another *Eozoön* paper when he died in November of 1899.

The active Eozoönist cause died with Dawson, although a futile attempt to revive it was made in 1912 by Randolph Kirkpatrick, a paleontologist attached to the British Museum. Little doubt remains of the inorganic origin of *Eozoön,* although encyclopedia and textbook accounts seldom declare its inorganic nature unequivocally; phrases such as "probably of inorganic origin" or "most scientists believe" recur over and over. This caution would seem unnecessary. The Geological Survey of Canada has studied the Grenville series in great detail and most of the questions so perplexing to nineteenth-century geology have been answered. A series of papers on the Precambrian of Canada, chiefly by Survey members, was published in the *Transactions of the Royal Society of Canada* in 1931. Dawson, the Society's founding president, would have been most surprised with the paper on "Life in the Pre-Cambrian of the Canadian Shield," which showed evidence that the laminated form of *Eozoön* was a "mechanical development" and that the alleged fossil itself was formed by the contact of Grenville limestone with igneous intrusives.

The *Eozoön* controversy is another example of the uncomfortable position of nineteenth-century science. During this century, in the field of geology alone, dozens of organized surveys made discoveries which challenged existing attitudes and opinions. *Eozoön* was one such discovery, the product of the Geological Survey of Canada. It was also in a very real sense the product of improved microscopes. Many of the difficulties over *Eozoön* were minor reflections of the problems involved in applying a new technology to the results of the great surveys. In this, as in many other areas, nineteenth-century science was sufficiently advanced to raise such questions, but insufficiently developed to settle them.

# VII. The Glacier Question

When Louis Agassiz told British geologists in 1840 that their country had a recent geological past very similar to that of his own Switzerland, he was thoroughly ridiculed. Nearly all geologists upheld the marine origin of the glacial drift in Britain. It was inconceivable to them that the same land glaciers which were moving down Swiss valleys could account for glacial phenomena in the strikingly different conditions of the British Isles. A great submergence of the land with subsequent glaciation by floating ice was much more likely in the opinion of these geologists. A vigorous controversy began after Agassiz's remarks in 1840 and lasted throughout the nineteenth century. Indeed, it was not until the early 1860's that the glacier theory found much acceptance in Britain.[1]

One school of thought contended that the climate of the northern hemisphere between the Pliocene and the present had been considerably cooler than either the preceding or following. This refrigeration had been accompanied by greater precipitation which, combined with colder temperatures, had produced permanent snowfields at higher elevations. Glacialists held that these snowfields gradually grew larger until they became the cause of still lower temperatures and still more precipitation. The cycle thus established was responsible for the period that came to be called the "ice age."

The rival theory posited huge icebergs to account for the marks on rocks and deposits of boulders many miles

[1] J. K. Charlesworth, *The Quaternary Era* (London, 1957) 2: pp. 614–633; Richard Foster Flint, *Glacial Geology and the Pleistocene Epoch* (New York, 1947), pp. 4–6. See also George P. Merrill, "The Development of the Glacial Hypothesis in America," *Popular Science Monthly* 68 (April, 1906): pp. 300–322 and William McCallien, "The Birth of Glacial Geology," *Nature* 47 (March 15, 1941): pp. 316–318.

from any possible source. Those who held this theory accepted the notion of post-Pliocene refrigeration; in fact, they regarded this refrigeration as the cause of the great icebergs. The argued that there was considerable evidence that much land currently above sea level had been submerged after the Pliocene. According to the drift-ice hypothesis, huge icebergs grinding and pushing across the submerged earth had caused the boulder deposits and rock markings.

The controversy between these two points of view was in full progress at Edinburgh when Dawson studied there in the 1840's. He took courses from one of the most prominent drift-ice men, Robert Jameson. His friend and mentor, Sir Charles Lyell, held to the iceberg theory except in mountainous regions, as did the Director of the Geological Survey of Scotland, Sir Roderick Murchison.[2] Even before going to Edinburgh, Dawson had many opportunities to observe the glacial phenomena in the vicinity of Pictou. He and his younger brother romped over the great boulders along the Nova Scotia coast—boulders which were often moved great distances by floating ice almost under Dawson's eyes. With a background such as this, it was almost inevitable that Dawson would join the drift-ice forces when he began to write on glacial geology.

The first edition of *Acadian Geology,* published in 1855, contained Dawson's initial significant contribution to the discussion. Investigation of the Nova Scotia drift showed, he said, that "it strongly resembles, though on a greater scale, the effects now produced by frost and floating ice." [3] While continental glacialists could argue only speculatively, Dawson claimed the advantage of an appeal to causes then in operation. Along the Nova Scotia coast, floating ice annually took up loose stones and deposited them far down

2 Sir Edward B. Bailey, *Charles Lyell* (London, 1962), pp. 140–141.

3 John William Dawson, *Acadian Geology* (Edinburgh, 1855), pp. 51–52.

the coast. He testified to seeing stones ten feet in diameter moved far up beaches in one year from below the low water mark.

> Let us suppose, then, the surface of the land, while its projecting rocks were still uncovered by surface deposits, exposed for many successive centuries to the action of alternate frosts and thaws, [*sic*] the whole of the untravelled drift might have been accumulated on its surface. Let it then be submerged until its hill-tops should become islands or reefs of rocks in a sea loaded in winter and spring with drift ice, floated along by currents. . . . We have in these causes ample means for accounting for the whole of the appearances, including the travelled blocks and the scratched and polished rock-surfaces.[4]

Dawson was prepared with a wealth of local detail to meet most of the objections to the drift-ice theory. For example, it had often been noted that those who posited seas which covered mountains were logically required to posit icebergs large enough to scrape bottom at great depths. Since the water was thought to be 4,000 to 5,000 feet deep in some instances, this was most improbable. Dawson's response to this objection was that the land subsided gradually and that the drift and striation occurred while the water was very shallow. As the land sank, the pressure of new ice floes pushed the drift blocks successively higher and eventually moved them to the top of mountains. When submergence continued even further, icebergs floated over the mountains without touching. At this point the drift was no longer pushed by ice, although the rocks frozen in the base of the icebergs were often deposited directly on the very summits as the bergs melted.[5] Dawson himself, for example, had drift blocks practically in his back yard on Mount Royal.

The drift on Mount Royal and throughout most of the area in which Dawson worked was stratified and resembled

[4] *Ibid.*, p. 52.
[5] *Ibid.*, p. 53.

other, nonglacial, deposits which were known to be of marine origin. In 1857 he identified three levels of stratification in the drift of the St. Lawrence valley: the boulder clay, the Leda clay, and the Saxicava sand.[6] Dawson thought that it was only reasonable to conclude that the presence of such clearly stratified drift indicated that the same floating ice which was currently depositing drift each spring in the lower St. Lawrence valley had been responsible for the older drift as well.

Whatever favorable presumption was created by such facts was completely vindicated, in Dawson's opinion, by the abundance of marine fossils found in the St. Lawrence drift. Here he was convinced that he had positive proof of the correctness of his views. It was difficult for anyone to imagine a land glacier carrying along with it dozens of species of mollusks. The strength of this evidence led Dawson to collect these fossils avidly and to spend a great amount of time vainly trying to establish their presence in the glacial drift of the western plains.

Between 1857 and 1860, Dawson published three long articles in *The Canadian Naturalist and Geologist* on the fossiliferous drift of the St. Lawrence basin. He was especially interested in demonstrating that the fossil remains indicated a wide range of ocean life and, therefore, a wide range of oceanic conditions. The fossils of the St. Lawrence drift were not due to a temporary submergence of the river bottom, in Dawson's opinion, but rather to long, continuous submergence. For him, the long submergence meant that any ice in the valley must have been floating and that the glacial striation in the area must have been caused by this drift ice.

In his article in 1860, "Notice of Tertiary Fossils from Labrador . . . ," Dawson extended his arguments for drift

[6] J. W. Dawson, "On the Newer Pliocene and Post-Pliocene Deposits of the Vicinity of Montreal . . . ," *Canadian Naturalist and Geologist* 2 (December, 1857): pp. 402, 405.

ice to the meteorological level. He noted that extremes of annual temperature differed greatly on opposite sides of the Atlantic. The isothermal line of 40°, for example, passed from the south side of the St. Lawrence steadily northward and reached Europe near Drontheim in Norway. As a result of this difference, the descent of icebergs from the north and the drifting and pushing of boulders by ice occurred much more dramatically in North America. When geologists discussed the much harsher climate of the post-Pliocene period, they usually assumed, on the uniformitarian principle, a similar relation between North America and Europe and, consequently, projected extreme cold for Europe and a stupendous refrigeration for North America.[7]

Dawson disputed this conclusion. He argued that it did not necessarily follow on the uniformitarian principle that the changes of the past had preserved the same relative climates. The evidence, he said, indicated that a great revolution had occurred in Europe, while the change had been much less in America:

> In short, the causes of the coldness of the pleistocene seas to some extent still remain in America, while they must have disappeared or been modified in Europe.[8]

Modern geology was based on the notion of uniform cause, but this did not always mean uniform result.

The uniform cause in this case, Dawson asserted, was a change in the distribution of land and water. Lyell had shown that diminution of land tended to modify extremes of climate. Dawson applied this principle to the recent geological past of the North Atlantic. During the late Mesozoic era, this entire region had subsided gradually, he said, with dramatic effects on the climate. The waters

[7] J. W. Dawson, "Notice of the Tertiary Fossils from Labrador . . . ," *Canadian Naturalist and Geologist* 5 (June, 1860): pp. 196–197.

[8] *Ibid.,* p. 197.

of the arctic seas spilled over the American plains, lowering the mean annual temperature and diverting or diffusing the Gulf Stream. The deflection of the Gulf Stream, while effecting a further refrigeration of an already cold North America, had caused the climates of Europe to be much more drastically altered. According to Dawson, this meant that the climates of the two continents were very similar during the glacial period and did not, as was alleged by land-glacier enthusiasts, reflect the differences which currently existed.

Such a theory, Dawson claimed, accounted for all of the phenomena of the glacial period. Moreover, the theory provided him with a useful counter argument to those geologists who held to the land-glacier theory in North America, while admitting the drift-ice hypothesis for Europe. It enabled Dawson to apply to North America some of the convincing evidence of drift ice in Europe. At the same time, he could deny to the North American glacier enthusiasts the extreme cold said to be necessary for their ice cap. Dawson was positing, in effect, enough cold for icebergs but not enough for a continental glacier.[9]

Following this series of articles, Dawson wrote nothing on the glacier question for several years. During this period he was fully occupied with college work and turned his notes on glacial matters over to Sir William Logan, Director of the Geological Survey of Canada and a land-ice advocate.[10] His work was incorporated by Logan into the reports of the Survey in these years. Dawson did not take up the question again until 1864, when he devoted the major portion of an address to the Natural History Society of Montreal to glacial geology and admitted the great impact of recent glacialist publications (they are not named but are obviously the classic papers on Scottish glaciation by

[9] *Ibid.*, pp. 198–200.

[10] Sir J. William Dawson, *The Canadian Ice Age* (Montreal, 1893), p. 6.

T. F. Jamieson in 1862 and Archibald Geikie in 1863). Despite these persuasive applications of the glacier theory to the Scottish highlands, Dawson was convinced that "insuperable physical and meteorological objections" could be raised against the land-ice hypothesis in eastern Canada. He believed that he was able "to assert with confidence, though with all humility, that glaciers could scarcely have been the agents in the striation of Canadian rocks, the transport of Canadian boulders, or the excavation of Canadian lake-basins." [11]

Dawson could not accept the occurrence of an ice sheet at temperate latitudes when the area allegedly covered by the ice was so vast. The only inference which could be drawn from present conditions, he said, was that glaciers could exist at such latitudes only at high elevations. Furthermore, under probable conditions of solar radiation the great extent of the alleged North American ice sheet would insure absorption of sufficient summer heat to melt the ice accumulated during the winter. The only possible explanations, he said, were immense mountains which had disappeared—of this there was not a shred of evidence—or "some unexampled astronomical cause of refrigeration." Astronomical cause was likewise devoid of evidence and implied an insufficiency of the moisture necessary to nourish the hypothetical glaciers.[12]

In 1864 very little was known about the physics of glacier motion and the theory that a glacier could move because of pressures built up within itself was decades away from confirmation.[13] Dawson's insistence on the impor-

[11] J. W. Dawson, "Address of the President of the Natural History Society [of Montreal]," *Canadian Naturalist and Geologist,* N.S., 1 (June, 1864): pp. 221–222.

[12] *Ibid.,* pp. 222–223.

[13] For a detailed discussion of the difficulties encountered by nineteenth-century glaciologists in explaining glacier motion, see Israel C. Russell, *Glaciers of North America* (Boston, 1897), pp. 160–168 and Charlesworth, *The Quaternary Era* 1: pp. 108–125.

tance of elevation for refrigeration was accompanied by a challenge to glacialists to account for the movement of an ice sheet without mountains. Consequently, Dawson argued that it was physically impossible for a glacier to have moved hundreds of miles over primarily level ground. In back of his home on Mount Royal, there were feldspar boulders from the Laurentide hills deposited 600 feet above sea level. These boulders had been carried up to 100 miles from "scarcely greater elevation" and in a direction nearly at right angles to the glacial striae on the rocks between the Laurentides and Mount Royal. A glacier, he asserted, could not explain the deposit of boulders, let alone the phenomenon of conflicting striae.[14]

A continental glacier also required a degree of cold that Dawson regarded as unreasonable. Recent fossil discoveries—plants and land snails in the Ottawa valley, the various shells of the St. Lawrence, and fir-roots just below the boulder clay in Cape Breton—showed that the post-Pliocene cold in Canada was nothing like that proposed by glacialists, but was, rather, very similar to that of present-day Labrador.[15]

Dawson was confident that the glacier enthusiasts could not meet these objections. However, his most important arguments were contained in a long discussion of the various directions of the striation in the St. Lawrence region. Here, he thought, the powerful objections against the glacier theory were accompanied by a convincing positive explanation provided by floating ice. The same set of facts which disproved one theory proved the other.

Geologists were agreed that the glacial striation of northeastern America was in two main directions: from northeast to southwest and from northwest to southeast. It was Daw-

[14] Dawson, "Address of the President of the Natural History Society [of Montreal]" (1864), pp. 223–224.

[15] *Ibid.*, p. 224.

son's contention that the movement of glaciers could not have left such marks. The dominant direction of striation in the St. Lawrence region was from northeast to southwest, with another series of markings running from Georgian Bay down the Ottawa valley and across the flat plain on the south bank of the St. Lawrence and into the hilly region known as the Eastern Townships. These secondary markings were at nearly right angles to the main striation.[16]

Dawson noted that there was no question that the direction of the striation in the St. Lawrence was against the slope of the valley, i.e., from the ocean towards the interior. He thought this fact disposed of the glacier theory, while, at the same time, it was "eminently favorable to the idea of ocean drift." As the current of water carried drift ice up the valley the ice would have grounded on the shallower points upstream, leaving the northeast to southwest striation. Under these same conditions, a glacier would come to a halt and leave no marks. Further west in the same direction, the Great Lakes' basins were, said Dawson, easily explained by the cutting power of such deep, cold ocean currents, while the scouring ability of glaciers was very doubtful and, in any case, depended on great heights of land in order to gain sufficient momentum.[17]

The diluvial hypothesis also explained the secondary striation from northwest to southeast along the Ottawa River. Dawson asserted that during both the submergence and re-elevation of the post-Pliocene there must have come a time when the arctic current was obstructed in its course down the St. Lawrence and over the American plains. When this happened, the current was forced to change direction and follow the lowest land levels in a northwest to southeast direction. The drift ice carried along these channels caused the secondary striation. The channels them-

[16] *Ibid.*, pp. 225–226.
[17] *Ibid.*, pp. 226–227.

selves eventually became the valleys of Lake Champlain and of the Ottawa, Mohawk, and Connecticut rivers.[18]

Dawson did not exclude glaciers from his theory; in fact, he accepted them as very likely in local conditions. He argued that, when the continent had sunk so low that only its highest peaks were above water, the air would have been very moist and the temperature so cold that permanent ice may have formed. However, Dawson thought that the extent of these glaciers was insignificant. He scoffed at those who claimed to find the deposits of glaciers in every New England pasture:

> I think that most of the alleged instances of the effects of glaciers must be founded on error, and that old sea-beaches have been mistaken for moraines. I have failed to find even in the White Mountains any distinct sign of glacier action, though the action of the ocean-breakers is visible almost to their summits; and though I have observed in Canada and Nova Scotia many old sea-beaches, gravel-ridges, and lake-margins, I have seen nothing that could fairly be regarded as the work of glaciers.[19]

During the winter following his address to the Natural History Society, Dawson examined some post-Pliocene shells collected by the Geological Survey of Canada near Rivière-du-Loup. The particular grouping of species attracted his attention, so that in the summer of 1864, while vacationing at Cacouna, near Rivière-du-Loup, he spent considerable time examining the shell deposits. A most significant aspect of the Cacouna deposit and of similar instances in Nova Scotia was the continuing deposit of boulders and the slow accumulation of boulder clay, with floating ice and water action responsible in both cases. A uniformitarian such as Dawson found it very difficult to accept glacialist conclusions in the face of this evidence.[20]

18 *Ibid.*

19 *Ibid.*, p. 228.

20 J. W. Dawson, "Notes on the Post-Pliocene Deposits at Rivière-du-Loup and Tadoussac," *Canadian Naturalist and Geologist*, N.S., 2 (April, 1865): pp. 81–84.

Dawson was certain that at Cacouna he had found "an indisputable instance of marine boulder-clay." Moreover, the boulder clay bore the marks of a deep-water deposit. The most abundant fossils in the clay were *Leda truncata, Nucula tenuis,* and *Tellina proxima.* According to Dawson, all of these organisms must have lived on reefs in deep water, since they were imbedded in the clay in perfect condition with valves closed. Many of the nearby boulders provided further evidence of the marine character of the Cacouna drift; they had been encrusted with calcareous parts of marine animals before being buried in the clay. No land-ice theory could account for facts such as these, said Dawson.[21]

After a working vacation at Cacouna in 1864, Dawson spent the next summer in Europe. There, as always, he labored diligently, taking notes wherever he went. The most important result of this work was a paper comparing the glaciers at Mont Blanc with the icebergs which frequented the Straits of Belle-Isle between Newfoundland and Labrador. His purpose was to show that the glacial drift of the St. Lawrence basin was completely different from that of the Alps and could not have resulted from land glaciers.[22]

Although he was interested primarily in the drift of North America, Dawson accepted the floating-ice theory for most of Europe as well. For example, he argued that erratic boulders found high on the Jura Mountains were not carried from the Alps by glaciers. Such a theory, he said, required that the Alps were then "vastly higher than at present"—a very doubtful prospect. More reasonable, he wrote, was the postulate of submergence. According to Dawson, a powerful sea current ran between the Alps and the Jura and was fed icebergs from the glaciers of the

[21] *Ibid.,* p. 83.

[22] J. W. Dawson, "Comparisons of the Icebergs of Belle-Isle with the Glaciers of Mont Blanc," *Canadian Naturalist and Geologist,* N.S., 3 (February, 1866): pp. 33–44.

two mountain systems. It was these icebergs which carried the Alpine boulders high up the sides of the Jura.[23]

Such speculations were not, however, central to Dawson's purpose in examining Mont Blanc. He wanted to pass as quickly as possible from the Straits of Belle-Isle to Switzerland and ask the question "whether Canada was in the post-pliocene period like the present Belle-Isle or the present Mont Blanc." Needless to say, Dawson satisfied himself that the present grooving and cutting of the beaches along the Straits provided sufficient explanation of the glacial debris of the whole St. Lawrence valley.[24]

Dawson compiled a long list of observations which, he said, showed the unlikelihood of the glacial hypothesis for most of eastern Canada. Whereas the glaciers of Mont Blanc heaped debris in abrupt ridges, the drift of eastern Canada was laid down in broad sheets. The material of moraines was "all local," while the drift of Canada was carried over giant distances. The stones in this drift were generally rounded, showing, said Dawson, the action of waves; the stones in true glacial drift were usually angular. The St. Lawrence drift also contained large amounts of mud and marine shells, neither of which were found in the deposits of land glaciers, such as those of Mont Blanc. Most important for Dawson was the fact that the Swiss glaciers always descended valley slopes and left grooves and striae which followed the slope of the valley; consequently, these glaciers always carried drift from higher to lower altitudes. The observed facts in eastern Canada, he pointed out, were quite different; there, the striae went against the slope of the valley and boulder drift was often deposited higher than its probable source.[25]

The Mont Blanc data helped only the negative part of Dawson's case; he could say definitively that the glaciation

[23] *Ibid.*, pp. 40–41.
[24] *Ibid.*, p. 37.
[25] *Ibid.*, pp. 41–42.

he observed in Switzerland did not resemble that of the St. Lawrence valley. On the positive side, he argued that the icebergs in the Straits of Belle-Isle were, in 1865, actively laying down sheets of mud, shells, and stones. Floating ice was grounding in shallow areas and grooving the surface below. Given circumstances more favorable for ice action in the post-Pliocene, it was very reasonable to conclude that more and larger icebergs had done for the whole of eastern Canada what the smaller icebergs were doing in the Straits of Belle-Isle in 1865:

> There is evidence that the St. Lawrence valley itself was once a gigantic Belle-Isle, in which thousands of bergs worked perhaps for thousands of years, grinding and striating its rocks.[26]

The climatic conditions which produced these hypothetical icebergs were the subject of Dawson's next paper on glacial geology. He made a survey of the fossil plants of the Canadian post-Pliocene to verify his theory that the climate of that period had been cold enough for icebergs but not cold enough for glaciers. Dawson argued that conditions in the post-Pliocene approximated the present climate of northern Gaspé and Labrador, a climate which supported icebergs but not glaciers.[27]

The evidence for Dawson's contention lay in a deposit of clay at Green River on the Ottawa River. More than a dozen species of fossil plants were found at this locality.[28] According to Dawson, such an assemblage of plants indicated a climate similar to that found presently between 50° and 55° north latitude. Some variation of these limits was possible depending on the direction of major rivers, al-

[26] *Ibid.*, p. 36.

[27] J. W. Dawson, "The Evidence of Fossil Plants as to the Climate of the Post-Pliocene Period in Canada," *Canadian Naturalist and Geologst,* N.S., 3 (February, 1866): p. 70.

[28] *Ibid.*, pp. 70–73. The species Dawson listed by name were: *Drosera rotundifolia, Acer spicatum, Potentilla canadensis, Gaylussaccia resinosa, Populus balsamifera, Thuja occidentalis, Potomogeton perfoliatus, Potamogeton pusillus, Equisetum scirpoides.*

though Dawson claimed that in the case of the Ottawa River deposit variation could not have exceeded these limits. Therefore, he concluded, these plants showed that the post-Pliocene refrigeration of the Ottawa valley reduced the temperature to nearly the same level as the present south coast of Labrador, where such a group of plants could presently live.[29] The fossil plants at Green River showed, he said, what he had maintained all along; the climate of the post-Pliocene in Canada was not as severe as glacialists believed.

When Dawson published the second and greatly expanded edition of *Acadian Geology* in 1868, he again advanced this position. He included a new chapter, "The Post-Pliocene Period," in which he extended the diluvial interpretation of the Nova Scotia drift which he had made in the 1855 edition. The new chapter was composed largely of material from the *Canadian Naturalist* articles in 1866.[30]

Dawson again published original research on the glacial deposits of the St. Lawrence in 1872. In that year, he produced a substantial monograph, *Notes on the Post-Pliocene Geology of Canada.* Recent reports of the Geological Survey of Ohio and of the United States and Canadian Geological Surveys were among the factors which led Dawson to publish his monograph. All three of these surveys had, since 1869, published research which was relevant to the glacier controversy. The three surveys had interpreted according to the glacial hypothesis evidence brought to light by this research. *Notes on the Post-Pliocene Geology of Canada* was an attempt to fit the new data into what Dawson termed the "moderate view . . . of Sir Roderick Murchison and Sir Charles Lyell." [31]

[29] *Ibid.*, p. 74.

[30] J. William Dawson, *Acadian Geology* (2nd ed., London, 1868), pp. 58–86.

[31] J. William Dawson, *Notes on the Post-Pliocene Geology of Canada* (Montreal, 1872), p. 104.

The *Report of the Geological Survey of Ohio* for 1869 had examined the post-Pliocene deposits in northern Ohio, particularly along the shore of Lake Erie. Since this area was contiguous to the province of Ontario and the post-Pliocene deposits of the St. Lawrence, Dawson was very interested in the *Report*. The author of the relevant sections of the *Report* was Professor J. S. Newberry of Columbia University, a very able glacialist. Newberry, in effect, presented a direct challenge to Dawson by interpreting the drift deposits along the south shore of Lake Erie according to the glacier theory. The Erie deposits were not only geographically contiguous; they bore a strong resemblance to the "Leda clay" of Dawson's St. Lawrence work. If the "Erie clay" of Newberry's *Report* was successfully interpreted in terms of a continental glacier, Dawson's diluvial interpretation of the St. Lawrence deposits would have been very tenuous.

Newberry's theory was eclectic. He insisted on continental glaciation and on the role of the glacier in cutting the Great Lakes' basins and the river valleys of the midwest. On the other hand, he was certain that the "Erie clay" had been deposited by water. He denied, however, that ocean currents, such as those hypothesized by Dawson, had been the agents of deposit. In Newberry's view, the post-Pliocene had begun with a period of continental elevation; glaciation and this elevation, he said, had occurred simultaneously. As the land subsided and the glacier melted, the lake basins scoured by the glacier had filled with meltwater. The "Erie clay," then, was deposited by this water—fresh water from an inland sea, not Dawson's arctic current.[32]

The points at issue for Dawson were, first, the very existence of the continental glacier; second, the time sequence of the glacial phenomena, and third, Newberry's contention that the "Erie clay" was a fresh-water deposit. On the first

[32] *Ohio Geological Survey 1869* (Columbus, 1871), pp. 28–33.

point, Dawson asserted that all of his earlier objections to the continental glacier were as valid as ever. As far as the time sequence was concerned, Dawson offered the following chain of events: elevation during the Pliocene, subsidence at the beginning of the post-Pliocene, a strong arctic current with thousands of huge icebergs pouring down the St. Lawrence, over the Great Lakes' region, and into the Mississippi valley. Erosion of the lake basins, striation of rock surfaces and deposition of drift were, then, part of one great operation. For Dawson, the arctic current carved the river channels and lake basins; the icebergs grooved the rocks; and the slower portions of the current laid down the much-debated "clays." [33]

Dawson cited again the Straits of Belle-Isle. Observation showed, he said, that for ten icebergs which entered the Straits fifty drifted south into the Atlantic. Yet, on a single day nearly five hundred huge bergs could be found in the Straits. Anyone who had difficulty accepting floating ice as the agent of striation, Dawson asserted, should first imagine the entire St. Lawrence valley in the condition of the Straits of Belle-Isle. If glacialists would then consider the probable effect of the post-Pliocene refrigeration in greatly increasing the size and number of these hypothetical icebergs, Dawson was confident that they would not look further for an explanation of the drift in Canada.[34]

In *Notes on the Post-Pliocene Geology of Canada,* Dawson addressed himself for the first time to the very damaging criticism of most glacialists that no marine fossils were found in the drift west of central Ontario. On several earlier occasions, he had implied his confidence that such fossils would be found. By 1872, however, it was obvious that his confidence had waned and he wrote from a more defensive position. He now explained how, even accord-

[33] Dawson, *Notes on the Post-Pliocene Geology of Canada,* pp. 5–6.
[34] *Ibid.,* p. 111.

ing to the drift-ice hypothesis, no marine fossils would be found in southern Ontario and the American midwest. Noting in passing that the absence of such fossils was also very difficult for Newberry to explain, Dawson contended that the "Leda clay" was always very poor in fossils, even near the ocean. The submergence and deposition might well have continued for a very long time before marine life could have spread over the entire area. He argued that, while no marine fossils had been discovered, much driftwood had been found and this was, in his opinion, "inconsistent with the occurrence of a general glacier immediately previous to the deposition of the clay," since such a glacier would have prevented the growth of trees.[35] It was even possible, said Dawson, that in many areas the supply of sediment had simply failed or that the relative levels of western and eastern America were different from those at present and that other sections had not been inundated after all.[36]

In addition to Newberry's discussion of the "Erie clay," Dawson had been confronted with new reports of both the Canadian and United States' Geological Surveys on the striation of rock surfaces in New England and eastern Canada. The new reports confirmed with abundant detail the widely observed fact that striation ran in conflicting directions over both areas. On the iceberg theory, Dawson said, the conflicting striation was readily explicable: the main direction of the striation, from northeast to southwest, was the same as that of the alleged Arctic current, while the conflicting striation resulted when the main current was deflected by submerged heights of land, causing the icebergs to follow lateral currents.

Dawson admitted that the glacial hypothesis might account for some striation. For example, he recognized the

[35] *Ibid.*, p. 6.
[36] *Ibid.*, p. 18.

possibility that much of the secondary striation had been caused by local glaciers. However, he thought that some sets of grooves simply could not be explained in this manner. At the mouth of the Saguenay River, at Murray Bay on the St. Lawrence, and along the Ottawa valley, there was, he said, no basis for assuming the existence of local glaciers. Heights of land such as the White Mountains or Green Mountains could account for secondary striation in New England; no such explanation was possible at Murray Bay or in the Saguenay and Ottawa valleys.[37]

As in every other controversy in which he was involved, Dawson stoutly maintained that scientific opinion was moving in his direction. With his own brand of clever, if heavy-handed, humor, he noted that the glacier theory had grown until "like the imaginary glaciers themselves, it overspread the earth." The glacier

> was even transferred to Brazil, and employed to excavate the valley of the Amazon. But this was its last feat, and it has recently been melting away under the warmth of discussion until it is now but a shadow of its former self.[38]

This style of humor irritated James Dwight Dana, who reviewed the *Notes on the Post-Pliocene Geology of Canada* for *The American Journal of Science*. Dana took particular exception to a remark by Dawson that the extravagances of the advocates of the land glacier had contributed to the overthrow of the theory. Although Dana seemed to take the remark personally, Dawson's thrust was aimed primarily at Louis Agassiz and the alleged glaciation of the Amazon.[39]

Dawson's book was also reviewed anonymously in *Nature,* where it elicited a cordial recommendation and a statement that Dawson had "added very considerably to our

[37] *Ibid.,* pp. 11–13.

[38] *Ibid.,* p. 104.

[39] James D. Dana, "Review of *Notes on the Post-Pliocene Geology of Canada* by J. William Dawson," *Amer. Jour. Science,* 3rd ser., 6 (July–December, 1873): p. 226.

knowledge of American glacial deposits." However, the reviewer dissented vigorously from Dawson's interpretation of the "Erie clay." Dawson's theory, he said, "can hardly be considered satisfactory." The clay had been carefully examined and had yielded no marine fossils, but, rather showed driftwood, old tree roots, and beds of peat. These latter discoveries indicated, the reviewer asserted, that "the probabilities are that the clay beds are of fresh-water origin." [40]

Dawson himself added a comment on his book in January of 1873 when he sent a letter to the *Geological Magazine* to clear up what he regarded as an ambiguity in his text. He had not meant to imply, he said, that the Great Lakes' basins had been carved solely by the alleged arctic current. He recognized that there were many indications of pre-glacial excavation, excavation by subaerial denudation. There was no contradiction, wrote Dawson, between such denudation and later erosion by the arctic current.[41]

In 1874 Dawson again vigorously asserted the diluvial theory. In an address to the Natural History Society of Montreal, he surveyed recent work by Professor A. E. Verrill of Yale (a protégé of Agassiz) on the invertebrates of the New England and Acadian coasts. Verrill had demonstrated the existence of isolated colonies of warm-water organisms which survived in very northerly climates. For Dawson, this was unmistakable evidence that the glacial age had been followed by a climate warmer than the present. Applied to Europe, "as it might easily be," Verrill's data provided a *coup de grace* to any hypothetical glacial period between the post-Pliocene and the present. Dawson had in mind a proposal of a second glaciation made by James

[40] *Nature* 7 (January 30, 1873): pp. 240–241.

[41] J. W. Dawson, "American Lake Basins and Arctic Currents," *Geol. Mag.* 10 (February, 1873): pp. 137–138.

Geikie in *The Great Ice Age,* a book Dawson described as resting "on the slenderest possible grounds." [42]

In his address in 1874, Dawson for the first time extended his diluvial theory beyond the post-Pliocene. He accepted James Hall's view that the sediments composing the Paleozoic rocks of the Appalachians had been laid down by arctic currents. Dawson even asserted that all of the land of the northern hemisphere had been subjected to cycles of subaerial disintegration followed by subsidence. During this subsidence arctic currents "scraped and peeled" the surface debris; "thus the carriage of material and growth of continents have ever been to the south-west." [43]

In a similar address in 1877, Dawson returned to the attack. This time he noted that the researches of the "Alert" expedition to the Arctic in 1876 had confirmed the tremendous power of floating pack ice. Investigations of the mountains of British Columbia by Dawson's son, George M. Dawson, had produced evidence of sea beaches raised to a level of 5,270 feet above sea level. David Milne Home of Edinburgh had recently shown "facts of similar import" in Great Britain and Norway.

> Geologists are thus beginning to realize the evidence of a prevalence of the sea over the Northern Hemisphere in the most recent of the geological periods; which at one time they would have regarded with the utmost scepticism.[44]

The third edition of *Acadian Geology* which appeared the following year, in 1878, contained practically unaltered the remarks Dawson had first made in 1855. It was not

[42] J. W. Dawson, "Annual Address," *Canadian Naturalist and Quart. Jour. of Science,* 2nd ser., 7 (July, 1874): pp. 280–282. It is ironic that data such as those produced by Verrill are today used by geologists as evidence for several glacial periods. See the discussion of the "Toronto Interglacial Section" in Thomas H. Clark and Colin W. Stearn, *The Geological Evolution of North America* (New York, 1960), pp. 278–284.

[43] J. W. Dawson, "Annual Address" (1874), p. 284.

[44] J. W. Dawson, "Annual Address," *Canadian Naturalist and Quart. Jour. of Science,* 2nd ser., 8 (July, 1877): pp. 294–296.

Dawson's custom to change his mind. The section on the post-Pliocene had doubled in size in the intervening twenty-three years, primarily through the accretion of the key elements of his many articles. The third edition contained a diluvial explanation of the post-Pliocene of Prince Edward Island, based on research Dawson had done a few years earlier with Professor B. J. Harrington of McGill (who later married Dawson's daughter, Anna). Except for the Prince Edward Island data, the new material in the 1878 edition came chiefly from Dawson's address in 1877 to the Natural History Society of Montreal.[45]

Dawson was silent on the glacier question during the next five years. During this period he published *Fossil Men and Their Modern Representatives* and his *Princeton Review* articles. He chose the occasion of his presidential address to the A.A.A.S. in 1883 to speak again on the question. The address, "On Some Unsolved Problems in Geology," provided Dawson with an opportunity to air his opinions on several matters. Among the "unsolved problems" were *Eozoön canadense* and evolution, although he spoke with a certitude which belied the title of his address.

This certitude was extended to the discussion of the Pleistocene period. Dawson left little doubt that he still adhered to the diluvial interpretation of the North American drift. One of his main targets was the glacialist use of Greenland as a model for Pleistocene America. For Dawson, Greenland was merely a "local case" in which extreme cold, high mountains, and heavy precipitation had combined to produce immense amounts of ice. It was impossible, he said, for the interior of North America to have received the amount of precipitation required for an ice cap such as Greenland's. Furthermore, the southernmost point of the Greenland cap was 60° north latitude, yet gla-

[45] J. William Dawson, *Acadian Geology* (3rd ed., London, 1878), suppl., pp. 19–28.

cialists required such a cover of ice as far south as 40° north latitude. Dawson denied that there was any evidence of such immense refrigeration.[46]

Dawson believed that proof of the validity of his objections was slowly emerging from the work of the Geological Survey of Canada in the western plains and Pacific coast regions of Canada. He pointed specifically to the raised sea beaches of British Columbia which, he said, showed the magnitude of Pleistocene submergence and re-elevation. Similarly, the great development of the "Missouri Coteau" in areas of the west where the glacier theory was "obviously inapplicable" indicated the likelihood of an inundation of the plains as the cause.[47]

Dawson's certitude wavered on only two points: the time elapsed since the Pleistocene and the original cause of the refrigeration. On the first point, he clearly favored a very short time (6,000–7,000 years), mainly on the basis of the condition of Pleistocene fossils. Out of solicitude for his audience's endurance, he did not pursue the question of chronology beyond this observation.[48]

Dawson was willing to discuss the causes of refrigeration at greater length. He once again spoke firmly in favor of Lyell's theory of climatic change as a result of alterations in the distribution of land and water. At this time the leading rival theory was James Croll's astronomical hypothesis which accounted for change in climate on the basis of varying eccentricity of the earth's orbit. Dawson rejected Croll's theory on uniformitarian grounds; it required causes which were not presently observable. On the other hand, changes in level and in distribution of land and water were occurring constantly.

[46] J. William Dawson, "On Some Unsolved Problems of Geology," *Proc. Amer. Assoc. Advancement of Science* 32 (1883): pp. 22–23.

[47] *Ibid.*, pp. 23–25.

[48] *Ibid.*, p. 27.

Lyell's theory had several additional advantages for Dawson. It could explain the coexistence of an ice cap in Greenland with a deluge of North America. Indeed, the greater humidity posited for the northern hemisphere was an excellent theoretical cause of the ice cap. In addition, Dawson's diluvial hypothesis required precisely the conditions which would have resulted had Lyell's theory been correct—more cold, more water, less land. If Lyell's theory had not already existed, it would have been necessary for Dawson to invent it.

Lyell's views on the distribution of land and water also formed an important part of Dawson's next contribution to the glacier dispute, his presidential address to the British Association for the Advancement of Science in 1886. The address, a survey of the geological history of the North Atlantic, covered an extremely broad topic; it was for the most part a non-controversial essay in historical geology. However, Dawson chose to pay special attention to the glacial age and his remarks on this score were highly colored by his own outlook.

Speaking to an assembly that was probably more receptive than his Minneapolis audience,[49] Dawson took issue once again with both the glacier theory and the astronomical explanation of the Pleistocene refrigeration. For Dawson, the rejection of the latter was clearly an integral part of his objection to continental glaciation. By 1886 he was explicit on this point. He now theorized that a subsidence of land in Central America had deflected the Gulf Stream into the Pacific Ocean. The effect of this change was to increase substantially the cold in northeastern America, while drastically lowering the temperature of western Europe. Dawson earlier had held that the cold arctic current of his diluvial hypothesis had continued south and had diffused the Gulf Stream. Both hypotheses provided him

[49] Charlesworth, *The Quaternary Era* 2: p. 620.

with a basis for his oft-repeated assertion that the present climatological relation of North America and western Europe did not exist in the Pleistocene. By 1886, however, it was evident that, regardless of the correctness of the diluvial hypothesis, the "Missouri Coteau" marked the southernmost penetration of either the glacier or the deluge. The subsidence of Central America, then, offered Dawson a geologically credible alternative to his earlier theory.[50]

The fact that a subsidence such as the one he proposed was so likely and explained so much led Dawson to regard the astronomical theory as unnecessarily complex. Croll's theory, for Dawson, was specially tailored to fit glacialist needs. He noted, for example, that a subsidence of the interior of North America during the Cretaceous period had resulted in warm water from the Gulf of Mexico flooding the Great Plains. The result of this change in level was a radical alteration of climate; during this period Greenland supported a temperate flora. Here was a case in which a change in the distribution of land and water had caused a change in climate as great as that proposed for the Pleistocene. Why could not the reverse have been true for the glacial period? This was precisely what Dawson proposed—a subsidence of northeastern America, rather than the warm Gulf waters.[51]

Dawson thought that the renowned *Challenger* expedition which had dredged the bottom of the sea between 1872 and 1876 had produced evidence which confirmed his hypothesis. The *Challenger* scientists had dredged glaciated rocks from a depth of 1,200 to 2,000 fathoms near 64° south latitude. In the Labrador current, a block of syenite weighing 490 pounds was taken up from a depth of 1,340 fathoms. Dawson defied his opponents to explain a

[50] J. William Dawson, "President's Address," *Report . . . of the British Association for the Advancement of Science* (London, 1887), pp. 25–26.

[51] *Ibid.*, pp. 26–29.

deposit of glaciated stones dredged from the arctic current 100 miles from land! There was considerable lithological evidence that this latter deposit was composed of rocks from the Precambrian and Paleozoic formations further north. Such deposits, he claimed, were obviously composed of stones released by melting icebergs.[52]

Dawson's argument in his address to the British Association was again a uniformitarian one. He had supported Lyell's theory of climatic change because causes such as those proposed by Lyell could presently be observed. Similarly, he saw no reason to postulate a continental glacier in view of the presently occurring deposits of drift from floating ice. For Dawson, it had always been evident that much greater cold, much stronger currents, and much larger icebergs, all a direct result of his Lyellian view of refrigeration, easily accounted for the glacial phenomena of North America.

Dawson's final statement on glacial matters came in 1893, when he published *The Canadian Ice Age,* a new and enlarged version of his *Notes on the Post-Pliocene Geology of Canada.* In his last book on the subject, he claimed that recent discoveries of Pleistocene fossils at high elevations and of the same species of modern shells on both the Atlantic and Pacific shores of North America were further indications of the correctness of his supposition that a subsidence of Central America had deflected the Gulf Stream into the Pacific.[53] He asserted once more that "there could never have been a sufficiency of snow to cause any general glaciation of the interior." In fact, wrote Dawson, meteorological records showed that an increase in cold in the north seemed to cause more precipitation to the south of

[52] *Ibid.,* pp. 31–32. It is interesting to note that a similar interpretation of such deposits was offered as late as 1912 by the great oceanologist Sir John Murray (a member of the *Challenger* expedition). See John Murray and Johan Hjort, *The Depths of the Ocean* (London, 1912), pp. 203–207.

[53] Dawson, *The Canadian Ice Age,* pp. 76–78.

Canada and that it seemed to be somewhat milder temperatures which caused the greatest snow in Canada.[54]

In relation to the glacier question, temperature assumed for Dawson the same significance that time had in his work on evolution; temperature was the point on which his attack on the land glacier was based. In this respect, it is surprising that, for all of the obsession with time in his other work, Dawson had almost nothing to say on Pleistocene chronology. When he did write on the dates of the glacial period in *The Canadian Ice Age* it was, surprisingly, to accept the conclusions of others. The reason for this was that few nineteenth-century glaciologists were inclined to extend the date of the Pleistocene glaciation much beyond 12,000 years. This time period was unrelated to the controversy itself, since it fit the glacier theory or the diluvial theory equally well. Although he clearly still preferred a shorter time lapse, Dawson reluctantly gave up his earlier estimates that the Pleistocene had ended 6,000 to 7,000 years ago. He saw no reason to dissent from those who had found that the rate of erosion in the Niagara gorge for the last forty-two years had been 2.4 feet per year. A projection based on these data gave between 7,000 to 12,000 years for the age of the gorge. The erosion at Niagara, according to Dawson, must have begun at the close of the glacial period, "whatever views we may take of the nature of that period." [55] Estimates based on the rate of deposit of silt in the Mississippi delta were very similar. Dawson also accepted a calculation made by Alexander Winchell, based on observations of the Falls of St. Anthony on the Mississippi; Winchell estimated that the Pleistocene had ended approximately 9,000 years ago.[56]

Dawson's untypical excursion into geological consensus began and ended with Pleistocene chronology. He was

[54] *Ibid.*, p. 84.
[55] *Ibid.*, pp. 146–147.
[56] *Ibid.*, p. 147.

very definitely not disposed towards the consensus view of the glacial age itself. He had not commented on the manner in which many glacialists named extinct bodies of water and wrote of them as if they were as real as the lakes of the nineteenth century; a minor extinct lake was even called Lake Dawson! There must have been a twinkle in his eye, therefore, when Dawson good-naturedly tweaked those who were "in the habit of giving factitious reality to their paleogeographical views" through such techniques. He produced his own "map," while admitting that the "personal merit and ability" of those at whose techniques he scoffed were "in the inverse proportion to the probability of their theoretical views." "Dana Bay" (after James Dwight Dana) was the great southern bay the shores of which washed the Missouri Coteau; "Upham Strait" (after Warren Upham) was the location of the great arctic current which passed between the Laurentians and the mountains of New England; "Chamberlain [*sic*] Sound" (after Thomas C. Chamberlin) led from the "strait" to "Dana Bay," while the "Gulf of Wright" (after George F. Wright) occupied the northern portion of the continent. Hudson Bay, said Dawson, was a meager remnant of the "Gulf of Wright." [57]

Aside from whatever satisfaction he drew from such sallies, Dawson took some comfort in the fact that, by 1893, scientific opinion seemed to be abandoning the idea of one great ice cap. His son, George Mercer Dawson, had shown that there were at least two centers of glaciation, one in the Laurentians and one in the Rockies. Opinion, in fact, seemed to be moving rapidly towards the view that two ice sheets moving from these centers, combined with numerous local glaciers, were the principal agents of glaciation.[58] In the rejection of the ice cap and, to a lesser extent, in the

[57] *Ibid.*, p. 78.
[58] *Ibid.*, pp. 23–24.

larger role assigned to local glaciers, Dawson could claim a measure of vindication.

*The Canadian Ice Age* received mildly favorable notices. The anonymous reviewer for *Nature* recognized approvingly the uniformitarian foundation of Dawson's argument: "Sir W. Dawson's requirements to explain the distribution of the Canadian drift are such as will seem moderate and natural to every rational uniformitarian." The reviewer welcomed Dawson's book "as a reminder that land-ice and enormous terminal moraines are not to be left in undisputed possession of the field."[59] A similar note was struck by the reviewer for *The American Naturalist:* "This paper is an important one and will probably correct the extravagances into which the past glacialists have fallen."[60]

It is fair to say that in addition to correcting extravagances, Dawson has achieved a modicum of vindication in the modern, synthetic explanation of the glacial phenomena of eastern America. Errors made by both sides in the dispute have been corrected by twentieth-century research. The "Leda clay" about which Dawson wrote so much was indeed a marine deposit. Dawson's assertion that his opponents could not account for the movement of an ice sheet across hundreds of miles of level plains was also valid; they could not account for such motion and it was not until the 1920's and the 1930's that a satisfactory account was made.

On the other hand, Dawson was completely wrong on most of his major points. Pleistocene icebergs, for example, accomplished none of the results attributed to them by Dawson. He was clearly incorrect in his deprecation of the cutting power of glaciers. He was wrong in his insistence that stratification inevitably meant ocean deposit;

[59] Dawson, *Nature* 49 (April 12, 1894): p. 553.

[60] Dawson, *Amer. Naturalist* 28 (March, 1894): p. 255.

it is now known that meltwater also explains the beachlike appearance of many moraines.

However, glaciology has advanced so far since the nineteenth century that a point by point comparison of today's knowledge with Dawson's errors is irrelevant. The sources of Dawson's misconceptions were many, but three stand out. First of all, there was his own monumental inflexibility. Secondly, lack of knowledge of the physics of glacier motion caused many errors. The third major source of Dawson's mistakes was his ignorance of the fact that there were several stages of glaciation. Scientists today know that the glacial ice advanced four or five times during the Pleistocene. The weight of the ice depressed the earth's surface which, in turn, did not regain its former elevation as rapidly as the ice melted during interglacial stages. Consequently, lowlying areas, such as the St. Lawrence basin, were inundated by marine waters.

The significance of these occurrences for Dawson's work is evident. Separate movements of the ice during different glacial stages explain the secondary striation which Dawson claimed was unaccountable on the single glacier theory in many localities. The warmer interglacial climates account for the presence of flora such as that described by Dawson at Green River, Ontario. Finally, the existence of several glacial stages has rendered untenable the topographical theory of refrigeration which Dawson defended so strenuously. Changes in level could not have occurred rapidly enough to have caused the succession of glacial ice and interglacial melting. According to Richard F. Flint, topography was important only in providing the high elevations necessary for the original glaciers which enabled the Ice Age to begin. Although the causes of Pleistocene glaciation are still hotly debated, there seems little doubt that the fundamental cause of the refrigeration was astronomical rather than topographical.[61] Far from being antagonistic to the glacier theory, as Dawson supposed, the marine fossils of the "Leda clay," the stratified drift, and the Labrador flora are, rather, an integral part of it.

After taking into account advances in knowledge since the nineteenth century, there remains Dawson's own stubbornness. While it is improper to apply to Dawson the standards of another century, it is not unreasonable to apply the standards of his own. It is true that he raised many cogent objections to the glacial hypothesis, but it is also true that he paid scant attention to the work of his adversaries; glacialist studies were very seldom even cited by Dawson. He seems never to have seriously considered changing his theoretical formulations and remained confident that his theories would eventually be proven correct.

Despite his confident assertions, even in 1893, that scientific opinion was moving towards a diluvial explanation of glacial phenomena, Dawson had become by this time practically the only champion of the older view.[62] As in most of the other controversies in which he was engaged, Dawson refused to alter his position. He used his great ability and vast energy desperately trying to fit new evidence to old theories. A Biblicist of no mean stature, Dawson should have known about new wine and old bottles.

[61] For lengthy historical discussions of the many theories of glacial refrigeration, see Flint, *Glacial Geology and the Pleistocene Epoch,* pp. 501–520; and Frederick E. Zeuner, *The Pleistocene Period* (2nd ed., London, 1964), pp. 173–207.

[62] Flint, *Glacial Geology and the Pleistocene Epoch,* p. 5. Flint states that Dawson offered the last scientific opposition in North America.

# *Conclusion*

THE RAPID advance of scientific knowledge in the nineteenth century stretched the fabric of consensus beyond the breaking point in almost every field. As a result, this century probably witnessed more scientific disputes and more controversy between science and related fields than any similar period in history. Sir William Dawson's career spanned most of this period and he was involved in many of its sharpest debates. In these debates, Dawson was motivated by more than the scientific issues at stake. His career as a controversialist evinced a wide range of personal, scientific, philosophical, and religious factors.

Despite these complex motivations, it is relatively easy to explain Dawson's involvement in the *Eozoön* and glacier controversies. Both of these questions concerned discoveries in the immediate vicinity of Montreal and, to a large extent, were based on original work done by Dawson himself. Dawson's indefatigable research and almost incredible range of interest brought him to the frontiers of geology. Frontiers of all sorts are usually centers of conflict and Dawson's career offers an excellent example of this generalization.

The rapid advance of science was responsible for a long series of clashes between older "naturalists" who were trained in the early part of the century and the younger specialists who were graduating from institutions such as the London School of Mines, and the new schools of science at Yale and Harvard. Lyell, Dana, Huxley, Darwin, Agassiz, and Dawson, to mention a few, were all confronted in their later years by younger specialists who controverted their findings. It was Dawson's fate to be one of the last of these "naturalists."

It is also important to note that the pace of research in many areas of study was so rapid that more questions were raised than were answered. The interminable quarrel over *Eozoön canadense* resulted in precisely this situation. This bitter controversy would not have been possible had paleontology been either more primitive or more advanced. Much the same was the case with the evolution and glacier questions. While it is a truism that science is always involved in a dialogue between questions and answers, it is fair to say that during the latter half of the nineteenth century this perennial dialogue was out of balance. The result was controversy and Dawson was too able and combative to remain on the sidelines.

This combative spirit provides another explanation of Dawson's predilection for controversy. Dawson's personality had a great deal to do with his work. He was a forceful man and he obviously thrived on vigorous exchanges of opinion. The heat of controversy must have served to warm the cold winters and even colder intellectual climate of Montreal, especially during the early years of Dawson's tenure at McGill.

Dawson's intellectual isolation drew him into controversy for more objective reasons, as well. For several decades he and Sir William Logan were practically the only accomplished geologists in Canada. As new discoveries were made in this region, it was inevitable that the two men would be drawn into the ensuing discussion. Both the *Eozoön* controversy and the glacier debate were directly connected to contemporary investigations in eastern Canada. Since Logan's work with the Geological Survey was chiefly of a practical nature, it was also inevitable that the theoretical questions would gravitate toward Dawson.

All of these factors are important in understanding Dawson's participation in controversy. However, in the three questions which touch directly on religious matters, geology-Genesis, polygenism, and evolution, there is an additional and crucial element. Dawson's role in these three controversies should be viewed in the light of his Paleyite approach to science. Dawson believed that the harmony of the Word and the Work was not simply a device of Sunday School pedagogy, a useful means of making religion intelligible, or a convenient metaphor. For him, this harmony was an objective condition and the Christian scientist worked under a moral imperative to find the nexus between the two theologies.[1]

This approach, so fashionable in the first half of the nineteenth century, was not popular with scientists when Dawson wrote his major books. More circumspect scientists in the latter half of the century despaired of harmonizing the two theologies. Even sympathetically disposed men, such as Gray and Lyell, believed that they were living in a transitional period in which synthesis was impossible. Dawson, however, would have none of this restraint and strove mightily to reestablish the links forged by Paley and Miller.

The scant support he received from scientists resulted in the marked defensive tone in Dawson's work. There was a persistent current of military metaphor in his rhetoric, especially in those controversies which touched directly on religious issues. He and like-minded men were always a "remnant" "holding the lines" or "defending the fortress" —a scientific band of Gideon.

Dawson's defensive posture was much more than rhetorical; it was often the controlling factor in his methodology. Defense of his position often dominated all other considerations. At his worst, Dawson employed a "method of tenacity" which belied genuine inquiry. At such moments he paid little attention to consistency or coherence

[1] J. William Dawson, "The Present Rights and Duties of Science," *Princeton Rev.* 2 (July–December, 1878): pp. 673–697.

of argument. For example, throughout most of the geology-Genesis controversy he based his position on the "verbal revelation" of Scripture. When he came to the Deluge and found this position untenable even according to his own very flexible notion of catastrophe, he casually adopted Hugh Miller's "visual revelation." Similarly, when confronted by his opponents in the *Eozoön* controversy with "eozoonal structure" of unquestionable mineral origin, Dawson resorted to denials of the resemblance to *Eozoön*. Yet most other scientists who have examined these materials have seen that *Eozoön* and its mineralogical cousins are almost identical.

Examples such as these could be cited on almost every major issue. Dawson was a very formidable antagonist, but at his worst he used what can be termed, a bit generously perhaps, an eclectic approach to methodology. Asa Gray was entirely correct in applying Harrington's famous couplet to this aspect of Dawson's work.

Dawson combined these eclectic tactics with a series of inflexible positions. If this seems paradoxical, it is only because the flexibility of argument was a direct result of Dawson's tenacious defense of these unbending positions.

This tenacity was, in turn, accompanied by a predisposition toward settled conviction. Dawson's eminent place in the small world of Quebec obviously encouraged this personality trait, for he suffered badly from a lack of day-to-day contact with men of similar scientific attainments. Dawson's inflexibility and tenacity were the natural result of an unhappy combination of personality trait, intellectual isolation, and the two theologies' tradition.

His adherence to the two theologies' tradition forced Dawson to search for scientific evidence of the Biblical cosmogony and of the Scriptural notion of a beneficent and contriving Creator. On the first point, he succeeded relatively well. His "modified uniformitarianism" proved equal to the task of accounting for most Biblical catastrophes. Where this approach failed Dawson fell back on his eclectic method of exegesis, and there was always the "marvelous flexibility" of the Hebrew language.

It was the second point, the search for a beneficent and contriving Creator, which proved most vexing. This search brought Dawson squarely into the path of evolution and the new evidence of man's antiquity. The old notion of the stability of species was regarded by Dawson as essential to the position that God took an active hand in designing the organic world. Above all, natural selection struck a fatal blow at both the contrivance and beneficence of God, in Dawson's opinion. A God who stood and watched while His creation perfected itself through random destruction was not the God of Abraham, of Isaac, and of Jacob.

The stress on the two theologies' position was greatest in regard to the creation of man. The concept that man had slowly and over a very long period of time evolved from brutish ancestors contained several threats to Dawson's cherished synthesis. The amount of time proposed by many paleontologists and archaeologists was far more than was allowable even on the most liberal reading of Genesis. Furthermore, if the concept of design did not hold for the most advanced of creatures, it was foolish indeed to look for design elsewhere in nature. It was unthinkable to Dawson that the same God who had created man in His own image and likeness could have allowed him to live as a brute for millions of years.

The many controversies over the human past bridge the gap between the evolution question and the early disputes of the nineteenth century, such as polygenism and geology-Genesis. From the point of view of the two theologies' tradition, this gap marks two episodes of one long battle. This fact is very important in understanding Dawson. He was almost unique in having an active role in both episodes.

Attitudes formed during the earlier controversies dominated his later work. Dawson always remembered that he had seen older, "orthodox" ideas return to scientific favor in the earlier disputes. He waited confidently until the end of his days expecting such ideas to triumph again.

Dawson's life was filled with many achievements. His resourceful leadership was the most important factor in the establishment of McGill as a major center of learning. He was the geological pioneer in the study of vast areas of eastern Canada. Almost all of his research was important for his own time. The portion of his work that was incorrect served as a basis for later more valid conclusions. As a controversialist Dawson provided vigorous, effective opposition, the kind of opposition which helped advance the interests of science. Although the scientific vindication for which he waited never came, Dawson had accomplished much.

# *Note on the Sources*

In writing this commentary, I have assumed that those sources which were most helpful to me would be similarly useful to someone else. Most of the scientific problems on which Dawson worked have been studied thoroughly since his time; consequently, the number of secondary sources available on these problems is immense. I have found it impossible to use all of these sources and have cited only the most valuable of those which I did use. This embarrassment of riches is not the case with the historical side of Dawson's controversies. For this side of his work, I have tried to indicate the more relevant publications and the list, while by no means exhaustive, is a fair guide to a critical discussion of the materials at hand. In organizing this commentary, I decided that the best course was to discuss some of the general sources for the history of geology and then to consider the sources for the separate chapters.

## 1. *General*

The history of geology has not received much attention from professional historians. Fortunately, a few notable geologists have studied the history of their science as an avocation, although it is striking that the more useful books appeared a generation or more ago. The oldest of these, Sir Archibald Geikie's *Founders of Geology* (1897), is a very readable account of the origins of modern geology. Geikie uses a biographical framework to trace the course of geology from the ancient Greeks to the uniformitarian triumph. Frank Dawson Adams' *The Birth and Development of the Geological Sciences* (1938) employs a more conventional historical approach. The account of the neptunist-vulcanist controversy is excellent. Adams' own field was petrography and this emphasis is evident throughout the book. One wishes Professor Adams had continued his work beyond the nineteenth century. Karl von Zittel's *History of Geology and Paleontology* (1899) is much more detailed and less readable. It is, consequently, more difficult for the general reader to follow. However, von Zittel does bring his account up to the twentieth century. This book remains the single best source for the history of nineteenth-century geology.

George P. Merrill's *The First One Hundred Years of American Geology* (1924) is, unfortunately, the only book-length account of geological endeavor in North America. Two chapters—"The Eozoon Question" (pp. 564–578) and "The Laramie Question (pp. 579–593)—are virtually the only secondary accounts of these issues.

A study of Sir Charles Lyell, in itself, would be very nearly a history of nineteenth-century geology. A definitive study of Lyell, therefore, would be very desirable. Sir Edward Bailey's *Charles Lyell* (1962) fills part of this gap. While an excellent book, it gives very cursory treatment to each of the many facets of Lyell's career. *The Life, Letters and Journals of Sir Charles Lyell* (1881, edited by Katherine M. Lyell) makes up for Bailey's brevity. The two books are complementary. One is brief and succinct; the other comprehensive and rambling. What is needed is a modern study which will do for Lyell what A. Hunter Dupree and Edward Lurie have done for Gray and Agassiz. An important article which deals with Lyell's most significant contribution to geology is Walter F. Cannon's "The Uniformitarian-Catastrophist Debate," *Isis* **51**, 1 (March, 1960): pp. 38–55.

## 2. *A Life in Science and Education*

The Dawson papers are on deposit at the Rare Book Room of the Redpath Library of McGill University. The collection has not been cataloged or even counted. It includes hundreds of letters for the period between 1840 and 1899, although the bulk of the letters are dated between 1855 and 1890. However, the papers are kept in chronological order in folders. The order is accurate by year. More precise chronology is not accurate; an attempt was made to arrange the papers by month and week, but the results provide only a very general guide. The Dawson papers are composed almost entirely of letters received by Dawson. With the exception of a few scribbled pages, he kept no copies of letters he sent. Dawson's letters to Charles Hodge are in the Hodge Collection at Princeton, while his many letters to Asa Gray are kept in the Gray papers at Harvard's Gray Herbarium. A scrapbook kept by Dawson early in his career which contains some of his important correspondence with Sir Charles Lyell is also on deposit at the Rare Book Room. In addition to the papers, there are considerable amounts of Dawsoniana at the Redpath and McCord museums at McGill.

Dawson's autobiography, *Fifty Years of Work in Canada* (1901), was edited by his son, Rankine. An altogether tepid book, it gives a very good picture of Dawson's early years in Nova Scotia and at Edinburgh, but does not reflect much of his career as a controversialist. Dawson was more fortunate in his obituaries. Frank Dawson Adams wrote an excellent account of Dawson's life in *Science,* N.S., **10** (December 22, 1899): pp. 905–910. Henry M. Ami wrote a fourteen-page account of Dawson's life for *The American Geologist* **26** (July, 1900): pp. 1–14, with an extensive bibliography of Dawson's work. A good bibliography is also contained in John M. Nickles, *The Geologic Literature of North America 1785–1918,* pp. 290–293.

Although not the work of a professional historian, George Patterson's *A History of the County of Pictou* (1877) is a remarkably good book and is very useful for understanding Dawson's background in Nova Scotia. *Montreal: Seaport and City* (1942) by Canada's great humorist, Stephen Leacock, seems to capture the flavor of nineteenth-century Montreal. Much the same is done for the McGill of Dawson's day in Cyrus Macmillan's *McGill and Its Story 1821–1921* (1921) and *McGill: the Story of a University* (1960, edited by Hugh McLennan). Taken together, these four books provide a crucial sense of *Zeitgeist* for Dawson's career.

### 3. *Dawson and His Controversies*

The following books provide a good introduction to the major issues in which Dawson engaged. A further comment on the relevance of these works may be found in the bibliographic notes on the subsequent chapters.

Archibald Geikie's *Founders of Geology* and Frank Dawson Adams' *The Birth and Development of the Geological Sciences* contain thorough accounts of the neptunist-vulcanist controversy. These two books, along with von Zittel's *History of Geology and Palaeontology,* are also excellent sources for the scientific aspects of the uniformitarian-catastrophist dispute. For the relation of this question to natural theology, see Charles Coulston Gillispie, *Genesis and Geology* (1951). Richard Foster Flint's *Glacial Geology and the Pleistocene Epoch* (1947) and G. K. Charlesworth's *The Quaternary Era* (1957) include short histories of the glacier controversy. The best introduction to the polygenism issue is William Stanton's *The Leopard's Spots* (1960). Studies of the heated controversy over evolution are too numerous to mention. For an introduction to the issues, scientific, philosophical, and theological, see Loren Eiseley's *Darwin's Century* (1958). There is only one good secondary account of the *Eozoön* controversy—George P. Merrill's *The First One Hundred Years of American Geology* (1924), pp. 564–578.

### 4. *The Word and the Work*

Charles Coulston Gillispie's magnificent *Genesis and Geology* (1951) is the best secondary source for the relation of Scripture to the geological discoveries of the early nineteenth century. Gillispie's book is especially useful in outlining the roles of William Paley, Hugh Miller, and the Bridgewater Treatises. He shows very clearly the drastic consequences of the heavy reliance Paleyite theology placed on natural science. As a result of this reliance, the attack on the older science became, for the Paleyite, an attack on theology; "materialistic science . . . cut the ground from under materialistic theology" (Gillispie, p. 135). *Genesis and Geology* deals almost exclusively with British theologians and scientists. The American side of the controversy is touched on briefly in chapter XI, "Science and Religion," of Dirk J. Struik's *Yankee Science in the Making* (1948). A better and more extensive consideration can be found in Conrad Wright's "The Religion of Geology," *New England Quarterly* **14** (June, 1941): pp. 335–358.

Dawson's contribution to the geology-Genesis debate is best seen in his *Archaia* (1860) and in the revised version of this book issued in 1877 under the title *The Origin of the World According to Revelation and Science*. *Nature and the Bible* (1875) is likewise a valuable exposition of Dawson's outlook.

### 5. *The Unity and Antiquity of Man*

The best source on this topic is William Stanton's *The Leopard's Spots,* a spritely study of the polygenism debate and of the social and political impact of the "American School" of anthropology. Stanton shows the role of these anthropologists in challenging the Biblical chronology and the notion of the sterility of hybrids. Edward A. Lurie's superb *Louis Agassiz: A Life in Science* (1960) is essential to understanding Agassiz's racial theories.

Dawson's most important publication on the polygenism dispute is *Archaia* (1860). The latter half of this book is devoted to a discussion of the controversy and is a very intelligent presentation of the monogenist position. On the question of man's antiquity, the most significant of Dawson's writings is his long review of Lyell's *On the Antiquity of Man* in *The Edinburgh New Philosophical Journal,* N.S., **19** (1864): pp. 40–64. A comprehensive and very readable account of Dawson's point of view is contained in *The Story of the Earth and Man* (1874), which is especially interesting because in it Dawson gives his brachychronic judgment of the major European cave deposits. The evidence of great antiquity that most scientists saw in these deposits was conclusively rejected by Dawson and the "wild man" hypothesis advanced in *Fossil Men and Their Modern Representatives* (1880). This book is crucial to understanding Dawson, for it shows him at his most extreme. It is hard to believe that the same author wrote the solid, unspectacular *Acadian Geology*.

### 6. *The Eozoön Controversy*

The only important secondary study of the *Eozoön* controversy is George P. Merrill's *The First One Hundred Years of American Geology,* pp. 564–578. Merrill himself was a minor participant on the inorganic side some thirty-five years earlier and his study is a good one. In following the *Eozoön* controversy, one can get a detailed account in the many contributions to the *Canadian Naturalist, Pro-*

*ceedings of the Royal Irish Academy, Annals and Magazine of Natural History, Nature,* and the *Journal of the Geological Society of London.* Nearly every issue of these journals between 1865 and 1880 contains some contribution to the discussion.

The less interested observer will find it more practical to examine Dawson's *The Dawn of Life on Earth* (1875) and *Relics of Primeval Life* (1897) and compare these books with Karl Möbius's articles on the structure of *Eozoön* in *Nature* **20** (July 17, 1876): pp. 272–275, 297–301 and *The American Journal of Science,* ser. 3, **18** (August, 1879): pp. 177–185. King and Rowney's views are presented thoroughly in *An Old Chapter of the Geological Record with a New Interpretation* (1881). Virtually all of the important statements on the question appear in these five works.

## 7. *The Species Question*

Secondary sources on evolution abound. The best general accounts that I am aware of are William Irvine's *Apes, Angels and Victorians* (1955) and Loren Eiseley's *Darwin's Century.* It is difficult to praise Eiseley's book too highly. He well deserves the place he has found in many rhetoric texts. *Darwin's Century* is a comprehensive account of the significance for evolution of nineteenth-century developments in many fields—geology, theology, genetics, physics, and anthropology. It seems to me that this book is the best general history of evolutionary thought. William Irvine's *Apes, Angels and Victorians* provides good competition for this accolade. It, too, is brilliantly written. Irvine is a master of the incisive phrase. His own background as a Professor of Victorian Literature is evident on every page. *Apes, Angels and Victorians* is a superb evocation of the Victorian *Zeitgeist* and is especially valuable in showing the cultural environment of Darwin's and Huxley's work.

Philip G. Fothergill's *Historical Aspects of Organic Evolution* (1952) devotes considerable attention to continental scientists, an attention often missing in other studies. Fothergill also considers the many non-Darwinian theories of evolution which are likewise commonly overlooked. His account of Lamarck and the Neo-Lamarckians is particularly useful and his survey of Neo-Lamarckian experiments (pp. 253–274) illuminates many of the great difficulties experienced by the nineteenth- and early twentieth-century evolutionists.

*Forerunners of Darwin: 1745–1859* (1959, edited by H. Bentley Glass, Owsei Temkin, and William L. Strauss, Jr.) contains a number of significant essays. Francis C. Haber's "Fossils and Early Cosmogony" (pp. 3–29) surveys the myriad explanations of the "fossil enigma" from the ancient Greeks to the eighteenth century. The same writer's "Fossils and the Idea of a Process of Time in Natural History" (pp. 222–261) continues the history of thought on fossils up to Lyell's *Principles.* Haber's second article is important in showing the link between paleontology and progressionist and catastrophist interpretations of nature. Charles C. Gillispie's "Lamarck and Darwin in the History of Science" (pp. 265–291) demonstrates clearly the manner in which Darwin differed from predecessors such as Lamarck. More precisely, Gillispie shows that, culturally and intellectually, Lamarck was not a forerunner of Darwin. Arthur O. Lovejoy's "The Argument for Organic Evolution before the *Origin of Species,* 1830–1858" (pp. 356–414) is an effort at rehabilitating the reputation of Robert Chambers and *Vestiges of the Natural History of Creation.* Lovejoy is very persuasive in contending that many of those critics (e.g., Joseph LeConte, Tyndall, Huxley, Romanes) who charged Chambers with violating the sacred canons of Baconian induction did not scruple to follow similar methods themselves. Lovejoy argues that Chambers has been unjustly chastised and that the nature of scientific progress makes it inevitable that at some point hypothesis will outstrip evidence.

In this same article Lovejoy maintains that there is a close logical and historical link between uniformitarian geology and evolution. This point is also made by Gillispie in *Genesis and Geology,* although the same writer tentatively retracts this judgment in *Forerunners of Darwin* (p. 266). A convincing case for the opposite point of view—that the non-progressionist aspect of uniformitarianism logically and historically implied non-evolutionary biology—is made by William Coleman in "Lyell and the 'Reality of Species'" in *Isis* **53**, 3 (September, 1962): pp. 325–338. Loren Eiseley's discussion of non-progressionism in *Darwin's Century* (pp. 108–115) takes a balanced position on this point. It seems to me that Eiseley is correct in attributing an ambivalent influence to uniformitarian thought. According to Eiseley, one effect of non-progressionism was to strengthen the hand of those who saw organic nature as stable, i.e., non-evolutionary. However, another and equally important effect was "the important principle of continuity and adaptive response" which evolutionists drew from uniformitarianism (p. 115).

A refreshing and somewhat negative critique of Darwin and his colleagues is contained in Gertrude Himmelfarb's *Darwin and the Darwinian Revolution* (1959). Himmelfarb energetically uses many of the classic anti-evolutionary arguments to show that Darwin and the Darwinians were unable to meet the objections raised by their opponents. Unfortunately, Himmelfarb often writes as if these objections were still valid.

Any distortion of the scientific record that one might get from *Darwin and the Darwinian Revolution* can be corrected with dispatch by Julian Huxley's *Evolution: The Modern Synthesis* (1942) or by George Gaylord Simpson's lucid books: *The Meaning of Evolution* (1949), *The Major Features of Evolution* (1953), and *Life of the Past* (1953).

There are several excellent biographical sources which shed considerable light on the history of evolutionary thought: A. Hunter Dupree, *Asa Gray 1810–1888* (1959), Edward A. Lurie, *Louis Agassiz: A Life in Science* (1960), and Sir Gavin deBeer, *Charles Darwin: A Scientific Biography* (1964). All three of these books provide much more information than conventional biographies. There is, unfortunately, no similar study of T. H. Huxley.

Dawson's spirited resistance to evolution can best be seen in selected articles, rather than in his books. Dawson's reviews of major evolutionist efforts are especially valuable: "Review of 'Darwin on the Origin of Species by Means of Natural Selection,'" *Canadian Naturalist and Geologist* **5** (February, 1860): pp. 100–120; "Insectivorous Plants," *International Review* **3** (1876): pp. 64–72; "Professor Huxley in New York," *International Review* **4** (1877): pp. 34–50; "Haeckel on the Evolution of Man," *The Princeton Review* **5** (May, 1880): pp. 444–464; "Continental and Island Life," *The Princeton Review* **8** (July, 1881): pp. 1–29.

Dawson's own creationist outlook is thoroughly presented in "Modern Ideas of Derivation," *Canadian Naturalist and Quarterly Journal of Science,* N.S., **4** (July, 1869): pp. 121–138 and in his Vice-Presidential Address to the American Association for the Advancement of Science in that organization's *Proceedings* **24** (1875): pp. 3–26. References to evolution occur throughout Dawson's books; however, the most comprehensive statement of his position is contained in *The Chain of Life in Geological Time* (1880).

## 8. *The Glacier Question*

Studies of the history of glacial geology and glaciology are rare. Merrill's *The First One Hundred Years of American Geology* has a very good chapter on "The Development of the Glacial Hypothesis" (pp. 615–642). William McCallien's "The Birth of Glacial Geology" in *Nature* **147** (March 15, 1941): pp. 316–318 is a very brief but helpful account. Several of the scientific studies of the Pleistocene period include significant historical sketches. Two of these books, J. K. Charlesworth's *The Quaternary Era* and Richard Foster Flint's *Glacial Geology and the Pleistocene Epoch,* also provide an excellent scientific introduction to glaciology and glacial geology. The sections on North American glaciers in Thomas H. Clark and Colin W. Stearn's *Geological Evolution of North America* (2nd ed., 1968) are likewise very useful.

Most of Dawson's important contributions on glaciers are contained in the chapters on the post-Pliocene in successive editions of *Acadian Geology* (1855, 1868, 1878, 1891). More detailed information can be found in two book length studies: *Notes on the Post-Pliocene Geology of Canada* (1872) and *The Canadian Ice Age* (1893).

# *Bibliography*

## BOOKS


ADAMS, FRANK D. 1938. *The Birth and Development of the Geological Sciences* (Baltimore).

AGASSIZ, ELIZABETH CARY (ed.). 1885. *Louis Agassiz: His Life and Correspondence* (2 v., Boston).

AGASSIZ, LOUIS. 1857. *Contributions to the Natural History of the United States of America* (Boston) 1.

ANDREWS, HENRY N., JR. 1947. *Ancient Plants* (Ithaca).

ARBER, E. A. NEWELL. 1921. *Devonian Floras* (Cambridge).

BAILEY, SIR EDWARD B. 1962. *Charles Lyell* (London).

The Bible, Authorized King James Version.

CHAMBERS, ROBERT. 1858. *Vestiges of the Natural History of Creation* (New York).

CHARLESWORTH, J. K. 1957. *The Quaternary Era* (2 v., London).

CLARK, THOMAS H., and COLIN W. STEARN. 1968. *The Geological Evolution of North America* (2nd ed., New York).

CLARKE, JOHN M. 1921. *James Hall of Albany* (Albany).

COMMAGER, HENRY STEELE. 1950. *The American Mind* (New Haven).

CURTI, MERLE. 1963. *The Growth of American Thought* (3rd ed., New York).

CUSHING, HARVEY. 1925. *The Life of Sir William Osler* (Oxford).

DARRAH, WILLIAM C. 1960. *Principles of Paleobotany* (2nd ed., New York).

DARWIN, CHARLES. 1846. *Journal of Researches into the Natural History and Geology of the Countries Visited During the Voyage of the H.M.S. Beagle* (New York).

—— 1868. *The Variation of Animals and Plants Under Domestication* (2 v., New York).

—— 1873. *The Origin of Species* (6th ed., New York).

—— 1874. *The Descent of Man* (New York).

——1896. *Insectivorous Plants* (New York).

—— 1964. *On the Origin of Species, a facsimile of the first edition* (Cambridge).

—— 1966. *The Power of Movement in Plants* (New York).

DARWIN, FRANCIS (ed.). 1888. *The Life and Letters of Charles Darwin* (New York).

DAWKINS, W. BOYD. 1874. *Cave Hunting* (London).

DAWSON, J. WILLIAM. 1855. *Acadian Geology* (Edinburgh).

—— 1860. *Archaia* (Montreal).

—— 1863. *Air Breathers of the Coal Period* (Montreal).

—— 1868. *Acadian Geology* (2nd ed., London).

—— 1872. *Notes on the Post-Pliocene Geology of Canada* (Montreal).

—— 1874. *The Story of Earth and Man* (New York).

—— 1875. *Life's Dawn on Earth* (London).

—— 1875. *Nature and the Bible* (New York).

—— 1877. *The Origin of the World According to Revelation and Science* (New York).

—— 1878. *Acadian Geology* (3rd ed., London).

—— 1880. *The Chain of Life in Geological Time* (London).
—— 1880. *Fossil Men and Their Modern Representatives* (London).
—— 1882. *Facts and Fancies in Modern Science* (Philadelphia).
—— 1888. *The Geological History of Plants* (New York).
—— 1889. *Modern Science in Bible Lands* (New York).
—— 1891. *The Geology of Nova Scotia, New Brunswick, and Prince Edward Island or Acadian Geology* (4th ed., London).
—— 1893. *The Canadian Ice Age* (Montreal).
—— 1894. *The Meeting Place of Geology and History* (London).
—— 1895. *Eden Lost and Won* (London).
—— 1895. *The Historical Deluge* (Chicago).
—— 1897. *Relics of Primeval Life* (New York).
—— 1901. *Fifty Years of Work in Canada* (London).
DEBEER, SIR GAVIN. 1964. *Charles Darwin: A Scientific Biography* (New York).
DOBZHANSKY, THEODOSIUS. 1959. *Evolution, Genetics, and Man* (New York).
DUPREE, A. HUNTER. 1959. *Asa Gray 1810–1888* (Cambridge).
DYSON, JAMES L. 1962. *The World of Ice* (New York).
EISELEY, LOREN. 1958. *Darwin's Century* (Garden City).
FENTON, CARROL LANE, and MILDRED ADAMS FENTON. 1945. *The Story of the Great Geologists* (Garden City).
FISHER, RONALD. 1939. *The Genetical Theory of Natural Selection* (Oxford).
FLINT, RICHARD FOSTER. 1947. *Glacial Geology and the Pleistocene Epoch* (New York).
FOTHERGILL, PHILIP G. 1952. *Historical Aspects of Organic Evolution* (London).
—— 1961. *Evolution and Christians* (London).
GAMOW, GEORGE. 1963. *A Planet Called Earth* (New York).
GEIKIE, SIR ARCHIBALD. 1897. *Founders of Geology* (London).
GILLISPIE, CHARLES C. 1951. *Genesis and Geology* (Cambridge).
GILMAN, DANIEL C. 1899. *The Life of James Dwight Dana* (New York).
GLADSTONE, W. F. 1890. *The Impregnable Rock of Holy Scripture* (London).
GLASS, H. BENTLEY, OWSEI TEMKIN, and WILLIAM L. STRAUSS, JR. (eds.). 1959. *Forerunners of Darwin: 1745–1859* (Baltimore).
GRAY, ASA. 1880. *Natural Science and Religion* (New York).
—— 1889. *The Scientific Papers of Asa Gray,* ed. Charles S. Sargent (2 v., Boston).
—— 1963. *Darwiniana,* ed. A. Hunter Dupree (Cambridge).
GRAY, JANE LORING (ed.). 1893. *Letters of Asa Gray* (2 v., Boston).
GREENE, J. C. 1961. *Darwin and the Modern World View* (Baton Rouge).
GRUBER, JACOB W. 1960. *A Conscience in Conflict: The Life of St. George Jackson Mivart* (New York).
HAECKEL, ERNST. 1879. *The Evolution of Man* (2 v., New York).
HALLOWELL, A. IRVING. 1960. *The Beginnings of Anthropology in America* (Evanston).
HIMMELFARB, GERTRUDE. 1959. *Darwin and the Darwinian Revolution* (London).
HITCHCOCK, EDWARD. 1851. *The Religion of Geology* (Boston).
HODGE, CHARLES. 1874. *What Is Darwinism?* (New York).
HODGEN, MARGARET T. 1964. *Early Anthropology in the Sixteenth and Seventeenth Centuries* (Philadelphia).
HOFSTADTER, RICHARD. 1945. *Social Darwinism in American Thought 1860–1915* (Philadelphia).
HUXLEY, JULIAN. 1942. *Evolution: The Modern Synthesis* (New York).
HUXLEY, LEONARD (ed.). 1900. *Life and Letters of Thomas Henry Huxley* (2 v., New York).

HUXLEY, THOMAS H. 1899. *Science and Christian Tradition* (New York).
—— 1899. *Science and Hebrew Tradition* (New York).
—— 1908. *Darwiniana Essays* (New York).
IRVINE, WILLIAM. 1955. *Apes, Angels and Victorians* (New York).
JAFFE, BERNARD. 1944. *Men of Science in America* (New York).
JEPSEN, GLENN L., GEORGE GAYLORD SIMPSON, and ERNST MAYR (eds.). 1963. *Genetics, Paleontology and Evolution* (New York).
JONES, RICHARD F. 1936. *Ancients and Moderns* (St. Louis).
KING, WILLIAM, and THOMAS ROWNEY. 1881. *An Old Chapter of the Geological Record with a New Interpretation* (London).
LEACOCK, STEPHEN. 1942. *Montreal: Seaport and City* (Garden City).
LOVEJOY, ARTHUR O. 1936. *The Great Chain of Being* (Cambridge).
LURIE, EDWARD A. 1960. *Louis Agassiz: A Life in Science* (Chicago).
LYELL, CHARLES. 1845. *Travels in North America* (New York).
—— 1863. *The Geological Evidences of the Antiquity of Man* (London).
—— 1868. *Elements of Geology* (6th ed., New York).
LYELL, KATHERINE M. (ed.). 1881. *Life, Letters and Journals of Sir Charles Lyell* (2 v., London).
MCLENNAN, HUGH. 1960. *McGill: the Story of a University* (London).
MACMILLAN, CYRUS. 1921. *McGill and Its Story 1821–1921* (London).
MERRILL, GEORGE P. 1924. *The First One Hundred Years of American Geology* (New Haven).
MILLER, HUGH. 1850. *The Footprints of the Creator* (Boston).
—— 1857. *The Testimony of the Rocks* (New York).
MURRAY, JOHN, and JOHAN HJORT. 1912. *The Depths of the Ocean* (London).
NICKLES, JOHN M. 1923. *Geologic Literature on North America 1785–1918* (2 v., Washington).
NICHOLSON, H. ALLEYNE. 1896. *The Ancient Life-History of the Earth* (New York).
NORDENSKIÖLD, ERIK. 1929. *The History of Biology* (New York).
*Ohio Geological Survey 1869*. 1871. (Columbus).
OSBORN, HENRY FAIRFIELD. 1931. *Cope: Master Naturalist* (Princeton).
PACKARD, ALPHEUS S. 1901. *Lamarck: The Founder of Evolution* (New York).
PALEY, WILLIAM. 1837. *Natural Theology: or Evidence of the Existence and Attributes of the Deity Collected from the Appearances of Nature* (Boston).
PATTERSON, GEORGE. 1877. *A History of the County of Pictou* (Montreal).
PECKHAM, MORSE (ed.). 1959. *The Origin of Species by Charles Darwin: A Variorum Text* (Philadelphia).
PENNIMAN, THOMAS K. 1965. *A Hundred Years of Anthropology* (3rd ed., London).
PUTNAM, WILLIAM C. 1964. *Geology* (New York).
REINGOLD, NATHAN (ed.). 1964. *Science in Nineteenth-Century America* (New York).
ROSS, HERBERT H. 1962. *A Synthesis of Evolutionary Theory* (Englewood Cliffs).
ROYAL SOCIETY OF CANADA. 1932. *Fifty Years Retrospect* (n.p.).
RUDOLPH, FREDERICK. 1962. *The American College and University* (New York).
RUSSELL, ISRAEL O. 1897. *Glaciers of North America* (Boston).
SCHAFF, PHILIP, and S. IRENEAEUS PRIME (eds.). 1874. *History, Essays, Orations, and Other Documents of the Sixth General Conference of the Evangelical Alliance* (New York).
SCHUCHERT, CHARLES, and CLARA M. LEVENE. 1940. *O. C. Marsh, Pioneer in Paleontology* (New Haven).
SCOTT, DUKINFIELD HENRY. 1924. *Extinct Plants and Problems of Evolution* (London).

SHALER, NATHANIEL SOUTHGATE. 1909. *The Autobiography of Nathaniel Southgate Shaler* (Boston).
SLOANE, WILLIAM MILLIGAN. 1896. *The Life of James McCosh* (New York).
SIMPSON, GEORGE GAYLORD. 1949. *The Meaning of Evolution* (New Haven).
—— 1953. *Life of the Past* (New Haven).
—— 1953. *The Major Features of Evolution* (New York).
STANTON, WILLIAM. 1960. *The Leopard's Spots* (Chicago).
STRUIK, DIRK J. 1948. *Yankee Science in the Making* (Boston).
TAX, SOL, and CHARLES CALLENDER (eds.). 1960. *Evolution after Darwin* (3 v., Chicago).
VON ZITTEL, KARL. 1900. *Textbook of Palaeontology,* trans. Charles R. Eastman (London).
—— 1901. *History of Geology and Palaeontology,* trans. Maria M. Ogilvie-Gordon (London).
WALLACE, ALFRED RUSSEL. 1881. *Island Life* (New York).
WERTENBAKER, THOMAS J. 1946. *Princeton: 1746–1896* (Princeton).
WESTON, THOMAS C. 1899. *Reminiscences Among the Rocks* (Toronto).
WHITE, ANDREW D. 1896. *A History of the Warfare of Science with Theology in Christendom* (New York).
WOODWARD, HORACE B. 1907. *The History of the Geological Society of London* (London).
ZEUNER, FREDRICK E. 1964. *The Pleistocene Period* (2nd ed., London).

## ARTICLES AND PERIODICALS

Abstract of "On the Occurrence of Eozoon in the Primary Rocks of Eastern Bavaria" by C. W. Gümbel. 1867. *Amer. Jour. Science,* 2nd ser., **43**: p. 398.
ADAMS, FRANK DAWSON. 1899. "Sir William Dawson." *Science,* N.S., **10**: pp. 905–910.
"The American Association for the Advancement of Science." 1873. *Nature* **8**: pp. 392–394.
AMI, HENRY M. 1900. "Bibliography of Sir John William Dawson." *Amer. Geologist* **26**: pp. 14–48.
—— 1900. "Sir John William Dawson, A Brief Biographical Sketch." *Amer. Geologist* **26**: pp. 1–14.
BURBANK, L. S. 1871. "On the Eozoon Canadense in the Crystalline Limestones of Massachusetts." *Amer. Naturalist* **5**: pp. 535–538.
CANNON, WALTER F. 1960. "The Uniformitarian-Catastrophist Debate." *Isis* **51**, 1: pp. 38–55.
CARPENTER, WILLIAM B. 1865. "On the Structure, Affinities anl Geological Position of Eozoon Canadense." *Intellectual Observer* **7**: pp. 278–302.
—— 1871. Letter to editor. *Nature* **3**: pp. 185–186.
—— 1871. Letter to editor. *Nature* **3**: p. 386.
—— 1874. "New Observations on Eozoon Canadense." *Annals and Mag. Nat. Hist.,* 4th ser., **13**: pp. 456–470.
—— 1876. "Notes on Otto Hahn's 'Microgeological Investigation of Eozoon Canadense.'" *Annals and Mag. Nat. Hist.,* 4th ser., **17**: pp. 417–422.
—— 1874. "Remarks on Mr. H. J. Carter's Letter to Prof. King on the structure of the so-called Eozoon Canadense." *Annals and Mag Nat. Hist.,* 4th ser., **13**: pp. 277–284.
CARTER, H. J. 1874. "On the Structure Called Eozoön Canadense in the Laurentian Limestone of Canada." *Annals and Mag. Nat. Hist.,* 4th ser., **13**: pp. 189–193, 376–378.

COLEMAN, WILLIAM. 1962. "Lyell and the 'Reality' of Species: 1830–1833." *Isis* 53, 3: pp. 325–338.

DANA, JAMES DWIGHT. 1873. "Dr. Dawson on the Post-Pliocene Geology of Canada." *Amer. Jour. Science,* 3rd ser., 6: pp. 226–227.

DAWSON, J. W. 1847. "On the Destruction and Partial Reproduction of the Forests in British North America." *Edinburgh New Philos. Jour.* 42: pp. 259–271.

—— 1857. "On the Newer Pliocene and Post-Pliocene Deposits of the Vicinity of Montreal . . . ." *Canadian Naturalist and Geologist* 2: pp. 401–426.

—— 1857. "Review of *The Testimony of the Rocks* by Hugh Miller." *Canadian Naturalist and Geologist* 2: pp. 81–92.

—— 1860. "Notice of the Tertiary Fossils from Labrador . . . ." *Canadian Naturalist and Geologist* 5: pp. 188–200.

—— 1860. "Review of 'Darwin on the Origin of Species by Means of Natural Selection.'" *Canadian Naturalist and Geologist* 5: pp. 100–120.

—— 1864. "Address of the President of the Natural History Society [of Montreal]." *Canadian Naturalist and Geologist,* N.S., 1: pp. 218–229.

—— 1864. "Extracts from the Address of Dr. J. W. Dawson President of the Natural History Society of Montreal." *Amer. Jour. Science,* 2nd ser., 38: pp. 231–238.

—— 1864. "On the Antiquity of Man." *Edinburgh New Philos. Jour.,* N.S., 19: pp. 40–64.

—— 1865. "Notes on the Post-Pliocene Deposits at Rivière-du-Loup and Tadoussac." *Canadian Naturalist and Geologist,* N.S., 2: pp. 81–88.

—— 1866. "Comparisons of the Icebergs of Belle-Isle with the Glaciers of Mont Blanc." *Canadian Naturalist and Geologist,* N.S., 3: pp. 33–44.

—— 1866. "The Evidence of Fossil Plants as to the Climate of the Post-Pliocene Period in Canada." *Canadian Naturalist and Geologist,* N.S., 3: pp. 69–76.

—— 1867. "Notes of Fossils Recently Obtained from the Laurentian Rocks of Canada . . . ." *Amer. Jour. Science* 44: pp. 367–376.

—— 1868. "On new specimens of Eozoon Canadense, with a reply to the objections of Professors King and Rowney." *Amer. Jour. Science,* 2nd ser., 46: pp. 245–257.

—— 1869. "Modern Ideas of Derivation." *Canadian Naturalist and Quart. Jour. Science,* N.S., 4: pp. 121–138.

—— 1871. Letter to editor. *Nature* 3: p. 287.

—— 1871. "Note on Eozoön Canadense." *Proc. Royal Irish Acad.,* 2nd ser., 1: pp. 117–123, 129–131.

—— 1871. "On the Bearing of Devonian Botany on Questions as to the Origin and Extinction of Species." *Amer. Jour. Science,* 3rd ser., 2: pp. 410–416.

—— 1873. "American Lake Basins and Arctic Currents." *Geol. Mag.* 10: pp. 137–138.

—— 1873. "Annual Address . . . 1872." *Canadian Naturalist and Quart. Jour. Science,* N.S., 7: pp. 1–11.

—— 1874. "Annual Address . . . ." *Canadian Naturalist and Quart. Jour. Science,* 2nd ser., 7: pp. 277–291.

—— 1874. "Notice of J. W. Dawson's Annual Address of the President of the Natural History Society of Montreal." *Amer. Jour. Science,* 3rd ser., 8: pp. 151–156.

—— 1875. "Vice President's Address." *Proc. Amer. Assoc. Advancement of Science* 24: pp .3–26.

—— 1876. "Insectivorous Plants." *International Rev.* 3: pp. 64–72.

—— 1877. "Annual Address . . . ." *Canadian Naturalist and Quart. Jour. Science,* 2nd ser., 8: pp. 293–303.

—— 1877. "Professor Huxley in New York." *International Rev.* 4: pp. 34–50.

—— 1878. "Evolution and the Apparition of Animal Forms." *Princeton Rev.* 1: pp. 662–675.

—— 1878. "The Present Rights and Duties of Science." *Princeton Rev.* 2: pp. 674–696.

—— 1879. "Mobius on Eozoön Canadense." *Amer. Jour. Science,* 3rd ser., 17: pp. 196–202.

—— 1879. "Points of Contact between Science and Revelation." *Princeton Rev.* 4: pp. 579–606.

—— 1880. "Haeckel on the Evolution of Man." *Princeton Rev.* 5: pp. 444–464.

—— 1881. "Continental and Island Life: Their Present State and Past History." *Princeton Rev.* 8: pp. 1–29.

—— 1883. "On Some Unsolved Problems of Geology." *Proc. Amer. Assoc. Advancement of Science* 32: pp. 1–27.

—— 1886. "The Probable Physical Causes of the Destruction of the Cities of the Plain." *The Expositor,* 3rd ser., 3: pp. 69–77.

—— 1887. "President's Address." *Report British Assoc. Advancement of Science,* 56th Meeting: pp. 1–36.

FLEMING, DONALD. 1959. "The Centenary of the Origin of Species." *Jour. Hist. of Ideas* 20: pp. 437–446.

FRAZER, PERSIFOR. 1888. "Report of the Sub-Committee on the Archaean." *Amer. Geologist* 2: pp. 143–192.

GRAY, ASA. 1859. "Extract from . .. Memoir on the Botany of Japan in Its Relations to That of North America . . . ." *Amer. Jour. Science,* 2nd ser., 28: pp. 187–200.

GREGORY, J. W. 1891. "The Tudor Specimen of Eozoön." *Geol. Mag.* 47: pp. 348–355.

HAHN, OTTO. 1876. "Is there such a thing as Eozoön canadense? A Microgeological Investigation," trans. W. S. Dallas. *Annals and Mag. of Nat. Hist.,* 4th ser., 17: p. 265.

HUNT, T. STERRY. 1871. "Messrs. King and Rowney on Eozoön Canadense." *Proc. Royal Irish Acad.,* 2nd ser., 1: pp. 123–127.

JOHNSTON-LAVIS, HUGH J., and J. W. GREGORY. 1893. "The Ejected Blocks of Monte Somma." *Trans. Geol. Soc. Edinburgh* 6: pp. 347–350.

KING, WILLIAM, and T. R. ROWNEY. 1866. "On the So-called 'Eozoönal Rock.'" *Quart. Jour. Geol. Soc. London* 22: pp. 185–218.

KING, WILLIAM, and T. R. ROWNEY. 1870. "On 'Eozoön Canadense.'" *Proc. Royal Irish Acad.* 10: pp. 506–551.

KING, WILLIAM, and T. R. ROWNEY. 1871. "On the Mineral Origin of the So-called 'Eozoön Canadense.'" *Proc. Royal Irish Acad.,* 2nd ser., 1: pp. 140–153.

KING, WILLIAM, and T. R. ROWNEY. 1874. "'Eozoön' Examined Chiefly from a Foraminiferal Stand-point." *Annals and Mag. Nat. Hist.,* 4th ser., 14: pp. 274–289.

KING, WILLIAM, and T. R. ROWNEY. 1876. "Remarks on 'The Dawn of Life.'" *Annals and Mag. Nat. Hist.,* 4th ser., 17: pp. 360–377.

KIRKPATRICK, RANDOLPH. 1912. "On the Structure of Stromatoporoids and of Eozoön." *Annals and Mag. Nat. Hist.,* 8th ser., 10: pp. 446–460.

LIPPINCOTT, J. S. 1880. "The Critics of Evolution." *Amer. Naturalist* 14: pp. 398–416.

LOEWENBERG, BERT JAMES. 1935. "The Controversy over Evolution in New England." *New England Quart.* 8: pp. 232–257.
—— 1941. "Darwinism Comes to America, 1859–1900." *Miss. Valley Hist. Rev.* 28: pp. 339–368.
LOGAN, SIR WILLIAM E. 1865. "On the Occurrence of Organic Remains in the Laurentian Rocks of Canada." *Quart. Jour. Geol. Soc. London* 21: pp. 45–50.
—— 1867. "On Additional Specimens of Eozoön." *Quart. Jour. Geol. Soc. London* 23: pp. 253–257.
LURIE, EDWARD. 1954. "Louis Agassiz and the Races of Man." *Isis* 45: pp. 227–242.
MCCALLIEN, WILLIAM. 1941. "The Birth of Glacial Geology." *Nature* 147: pp. 316–318.
(MCCOSH, JAMES). 1878. "An Advertisement for a New Religion." *North Amer. Rev.* 127: pp. 44–60.
MERRILL, GEORGE P. 1889. "On the Ophiolite of Thurman, Warren Co., N. Y., with remarks on the Eozoön Canadense." *Amer. Jour. Science,* 3rd ser., 37: pp. 189–191.
—— 1906. "The Development of the Glacial Hypothesis in America." *Popular Science Monthly* 68: pp. 300–322.
MÖBIUS, KARL A. 1876. "Professor Moebius on the Eozoön Question." *Nature* 20: pp. 272–275, 297–301.
—— 1879. "Principal J. W. Dawson's Criticism of my Memoir on the Structure of *Eozoon Canadense* compared with that of Foraminifera." *Amer. Jour. Science,* 3rd ser., 18: pp. 177–185.
READE, T. MELLARD. 1870. Letter to editor. *Nature* 2: pp. 146–147.
—— 1871. Letter to editor. *Nature* 3: p. 267.
—— 1871. Letter to editor. *Nature* 3: pp. 367–368.
WILSON, MORLEY E. 1931. "Life in the Pre-Cambrian of the Canadian Shield." *Trans. Royal Soc. Canada,* 3rd ser., 25, Sec. 4: pp. 119–125.
WRIGHT, CONRAD. 1941. "The Religion of Geology." *New England Quart.* 14: pp. 335–358.

## REVIEWS AND EDITORIAL COMMENTS

"Dawson's Archaia," *Biblioteca Sacra* 17 (1860): pp. 444–445.
*Archaia: Amer. Jour. Science,* 2nd ser., 29 (1860): pp. 146–147.
*The Canadian Ice Age: Amer. Naturalist* 28 (1894): pp. 254–255; *Nature* 49 (1894): pp. 552–553.
*Fossil Men and Their Modern Representatives: Nature* 22 (1880): pp. 82–86; *Amer. Naturalist* 15 (1881): pp. 154–155.
*Notes on the Post-Pliocene Geology of Canada: Nature* 7 (1873): pp. 240–241.
*The Story of the Earth and Man: Nature* 9 (1874): p. 180.

# Index